House of the Wannsee Conference

D1368119

Permanent Exhibit

Guide and Reader
– English Version –

Exhibition

Idea, book, layout:	Gerhard Schoenberner
Specific research:	Götz Aly, Klaus Drobisch, Annegret Ehmann, Wolf Mattausch, Sylvia Rogge, Johannes Tuchel
Exhibition design:	Jürg Steiner
Staff:	Claudia Rinne, Christoph Althaus, Christoph Musiol, Olaf Chrapal
Lighting:	Hasso von Elm
Technical equipment:	Museumstechnik GmbH
Photography and lamination:	Wolfgang Schackla, Studio für Grossfotos
Exhibition photographer:	Hermann Kiessling
Director of organization:	Johannes Tuchel

Catalogue

Publisher:	Haus der Wannsee-Konferenz
Editing/Layout:	Gerhard Schoenberner, Mira Bihaly
Translation:	Werner T. Angress, Belinda Cooper
Design:	Jürg Steiner
Production:	Hentrich Publishers, Berlin 2000

Haus der Wannsee-Konferenz Memorial
Am Grossen Wannsee 56–58, D-14109 Berlin
Tel. (030) 805 001-0, Fax (030) 805 001-27
E-Mail: secretariat@ghwk.de
Homepage http://www.ghwk.de

Open daily 10.00–18.00 hrs.
Free admission. Please call beforehand to arrange group visits.
Public transit access: Bus nr. 114 from Wannsee S-Bahn station

Table of Contents

Cited documents are marked:
● persecuted, ■ persecutor, ▲ witness

Cover photo:
First of the German child refugees arrive at Harwich, UK, Dec. 2nd. 1938,
Hulton Deutsch Collection, London

1. Dictatorship in Germany

On January 30, 1933, Adolf Hitler and his adherents took over the government, with the aid of the conservative Right. They were determined to abuse the power given them, and never to relinquish it. This surrender of the Republic to those bent on destroying it was only the final step in a process that had begun long before.

The radical racist movement calling itself the "National Socialist German Workers' Party" (NSDAP) had no original political platform. It styled itself anti-capitalist, but its ideology included all the most reactionary trends of the time.

What was new about the NSDAP, and what made it a leading force in the parliamentary opposition movement, were above all its aggressive propaganda, which exploited every tool of modern advertising; its paramilitary organization as a militant, belligerent party; and its totalitarian claim to undivided power in the state.

In all its spheres of activity, the party followed lines of thought traditionally hostile to enlightenment and emancipation. Its radically racist anti-Semitism was rooted in the theory of a "superior white race," destined to rule, that had been developed to justify European colonialism. The myth of "Aryan blood" as a basis for a "national community" (Volksgemeinschaft) that would reconcile existing class conflicts, the claim to a leading position in world affairs, the demands for "living space" in the East and for elimination of the Jews, had all likewise originated around the turn of the century. Numerous associations had even adopted "Aryan laws" excluding Jews from membership. Thus during the Empire and the Weimar Republic, precursors had already proclaimed the racist theses that would become state doctrine and law after 1933.

Furthermore, fears of modern capitalism and the working-class movement, disappointment over defeat in the First World War, and dreams of renewed military strength and national greatness were also widespread and susceptible to exploitation by Nazi propaganda. Finally, when the call went up for establishment of an authoritarian state, traditional education in the concepts of hierarchical order inherent in such a state prompted many to accept this demand as simply a return to the normal state of affairs.

Hitler's political slogans captured the spirit of the times and the imagination of the masses. He also received the support of large segments of the elites of both governing institutions and big business. They had never accepted the Weimar Republic, and believed their interests would be best served if Hitler took power. Thus Hitler was able to abrogate democracy because too few people could be found who were willing to defend it.

1. Precursors

In order to justify colonialism, Gobineau had developed modern racial theory in 1853. In 1899, H. St. Chamberlain came up with an anti-Semitic theory of culture. Dinter popularized racial anti-Semitism in 1917 with a rather trashy novel that had sold 200,000 copies by 1922. In 1920, the programmatic tract "Euthanasia" by Binding and Hoche was published, followed in 1921 by "Racial Hygiene," a standard work by Baur, Fischer and Hoche that strongly influenced Hitler. Between 1922 and 1943, a popular "scientific" work on race by Hans F. R. Günther had sold 270,000 copies.

2. Hitler in Power

Grunewald Stadium in Berlin, June 1933

In 1933, arms were raised in the Hitler salute in Berlin's Grunewald Stadium and many other places around Germany. Others stood with arms raised in front of storm troopers who had dragged them off to their headquarters.

With the "National Socialist German Worker's Party" (NSDAP) in power, terror against dissenters began. The initial victims were Communists, Social Democrats, and trade union members. Subsequently, anyone opposing the regime became a target.

3. The Initiators

In 1923, Rosenberg propagated his theory of a "world Jewish conspiracy." In 1925, Hitler revealed his objectives in his book Mein Kampf, which few people read or took seriously. Yet roughly ten million copies had been published by 1943. Burgdörfer, a statistician, and church archivist Themel were actively involved in "processing" the Jews. The commentaries on the racial laws by Stuckart and Globke provided practical guidelines for excluding Jews from society. Except for Rosenberg, none of these authors was brought to justice after 1945; some even resumed their careers.

Zehlendorfs Fritsch-Denkmal

Zur Erinnerung an Theodor Fritsch, den Vorkämpfer der antisemitischen und völkischen Bewegung, wird demnächst in der Theodor-Fritsch-Straße in Zehlendorf diese Großplastik des Zehlendorfer Bildhauers Artur Wellmann aufgestellt. Das Denkmal, das in Bronze gegossen wird, ein Standbild nationalsozialistischen Geistes, stellt den nordischen Kämpfer dar, wie er den Streithammer auf den Schädel eines jüdischen Drachen niederzuschlagen droht. Unser Bild zeigt den Künstler bei den letzten Korrekturen am Gipsmodell. Foto: H. Sonnenburg

"Der Westen," Berlin, August 4, 1935

4. Terror and Concentration Camps

After the Reichstag fire of February 27, 1933, mass arrests were made and the first concentration camps set up. With the exception of the Social Democrats and the arrested Communists the parties in the Reichstag voted for the Enabling Act, a law that served as the basis of Hitler's rule for 12 years. Henceforth, the constitution was simply ignored; democracy had abrogated itself.

One of the 50,000 arrested was the editor of the "Weltbühne" journal, Carl von Ossietzky. In 1936 he was awarded the Nobel Peace Prize. In 1938 he was released from concentration camp, and died soon after as a consequence of his imprisonment. Once it had silenced the nation's intellect and conscience, the regime had a free hand to engage in its crimes and in the impending war.

Ossietzky as a prisoner in Esterwegen concentration camp

5. The April Boycott

When the foreign press reported on terror in Germany, the government responded with renewed terror. On April 1, 1933, storm troopers mounted guard in front of all Jewish-owned stores and the offices of Jewish physicians and lawyers. The government justified the boycott as a response to the "Jewish atrocity campaign." In fact, it proved to be the first step in ousting Jews from all spheres of business and professional life.

■ *"Para. 3 (1) Civil servants who are not of Aryan origin are to be retired (paras. 8 ff.); if they are honorary civil servants, they are to be relieved of duty."*

"Para. 4 Civil servants who, based on their previous political activity, cannot guarantee that they will at all times unconditionally support the national state may be relieved of duty."

Law for the Restoration of the Professional Civil Service, Reichsgesetzblatt no. 34, Berlin, April 7, 1933

Opera Square, Berlin 10, 1933

Seghers, Kästner, Tucholsky, and many others were banned. Almost the entire contemporary German literary community went into exile.

Berlin, April 1, 1933

6. Book Burnings

On May 10, 1933, students and librarians in every university town "purged" libraries of all "undesirable" literature, throwing the books onto flaming pyres. Professors, fraternities, members of the Stahlhelm, storm troopers, and Hitler Youth members all attended this spectacle. The blacklists later grew. The works of Voltaire and Lessing, Marx and Heine, Freud and Einstein, Heinrich and Thomas Mann, Brecht, Anna

7. Hate Propaganda

The regional leader of Franconia, Julius Streicher, spread murderous hate propaganda in his anti-Semitic weekly, Der Stürmer. Founded in 1923, it had increased its circulation to 20,000 by 1933 and to 600,000 by 1940.

The slogan "The Jews are our misfortune" was coined by historian Heinrich von Treitschke (1834–1896).

■ *"Yesterday, Franconian regional leader Julius Streicher addressed approximately 16,000 people in Berlin's Sport Palace. An additional 5,000 Berliners were gathered in the tennis hall, the next-largest indoor arena, where the speech by Party Comrade Streicher was broadcast. Tickets to both buildings had been completely sold out days in advance."*

Westdeutscher Beobachter, August 16, 1935

Preis 20 Pfennig

Der Stürmer
Sonder-Nummer

...sches Wochenblatt zum Kampfe um die Wahrheit
HERAUSGEBER : JULIUS STREICHER

| Sonder-nummer 5 | Erscheint wöchentlich. Einzel-Nr. 20 Pfg. Bezugspreis vierteljährlich 84 Pfg. zuzüglich Postbestellgeld. Bestellungen bei den Postämtern oder bei zuständigen Postanstalten. Nachbestellungen a. d. Verlag. Schluß der Anzeigenannahme 14 Tage vor Erscheinen. Preis für Reklame-Anz.: Die ca. 22 mm breite, 1 mm hohe Raum-Zeile im Anzeigenteil... | Nürnberg, Reichsparteitag 1936 | Verlag: Der Stürmer, Julius Streicher, Nürnberg... | 14. Jahr 1936 |

Weltverschwörer
Die enthüllten Geheimnisse der Weisen von Zion

Das große Rätsel

Der Reichsparteitag 1936 findet in einer Zeit statt, die gekennzeichnet ist durch Unruhen, Revolutionen und blutige Bürgerkriege. Eine gewaltige Erschütterung geht durch die Welt. Verschwörungen haben sich in allen Ländern gebildet. Ihre Kanäle reichen hinein bis in die höchsten Stellen der Politik und der Wirtschaft. Politische Agitatoren sind fieberhaft tätig und verhetzen die Massen auf. Ein großer Teil der Weltpresse scheint geheimen Richtlinien zu gehorchen. Er steuert offen oder verdeckt auf ein bestimmtes Ziel los. Dieses Ziel heißt: Durch die Weltrevolution zum Weltkommunismus.

Wer nicht völlig mit Blindheit geschlagen ist, sieht die Gefahr ungeheuer und riesengroß am Himmel stehen. Ueberall zeigen sich die Zeichen der Zeit. Schon schlagen die Flammen des in allen Ländern angelegten kommunistischen Brandherdes da und dort zum Himmel empor. In Brasilien brach vor nicht langer Zeit ein bolschewistischer Aufstand aus. Er wurde mit Mühe und unter großen Opfern niedergeschlagen. In anderen Ländern Amerikas treten die bolschewistischen Agitatoren offener und gewalttätiger auf denn je. In den Vereinigten Staaten stellten anläßlich einer kommunistischen Kund-

Deutscher Volksgenosse!

Was hat es für eine Bewandtnis mit den Geheimnissen der Weisen von Zion? Woher kommen die Unruhen, die Revolutionen, die Kriege in der Welt? Wer sind die Drahtzieher des

Massenmordens in Spanien?

Lies diese Sondernummer und Du bist Wissender geworden. Und bist Du dann mit der Aufklärung? Gib diese Sondernummer weiter! Schicke sie denen, die die Judenfrage noch nicht kennen! Es soll das ganze deutsche Volk sehend werden. Es soll auch der letzte deutsche Volksgenosse wissen, worum es geht. Sorge auch Du dafür, daß dieses große Ziel erreicht wird!

Der Stürmer

Das auserwählte Volk

DU SOLLST DIE VÖLKER DER ERDE FRESSEN

Den Satan, der die Menschheit quält / Hat nur der Teufel auserwählt

gebung die beiden größten amerikanischen Radiogesellschaften ihren Rundfunk zu einer Revolutionsrede zur Verfügung. Der Staat Uruguay brach die diplomatischen Beziehungen zur Sowjetunion ab. Er wies nach, daß Sowjetagenten den Sturz der Regierung Uruguays vorbereitet hatten. In anderen Ländern ist der Bolschewis-

Die Juden sind unser Unglück!

8. Segregation

Mass rallies, however, were not the only approach taken to prepare the German public psychologically for the Nuremberg Racial Laws. In order to create the impression that the public itself had demanded legislative intervention by the government, the Nazi Party launched a large-scale campaign; signs were posted throughout Germany warning Jews not to enter restaurants, public parks, and entire villages.

Denunciation of "racial defilement" in the town of Norden, July 1935

9. The Nuremberg Laws

On September 15, 1935, the "Reich Citizenship Law" turned Jews into second-class citizens. The "Law for the Protection of German Blood and German Honor" prohibited marriage between Jews and non-Jews. A Jewish family employing a Christian domestic servant under 45 years of age could now be convicted of "defiling the race," as could any

couple trying to evade the law by marrying abroad.

10. "Defiling the Race"

The new laws provided the basis for innumerable additional directives, decrees, and measures by which the Nazi regime step by step deprived German Jews of their rights and their means of earning a living.
The Law for the Protection of German Blood unleashed a flurry of denunciations. In Hamburg alone, nearly 5,000 people were arrested and questioned, and 1,500 judicial inquiries were initiated; however, only 538 people were convicted altogether in Hamburg, Frankfurt, and Cologne. There are no overall figures for the German Reich as a whole. The weekly Der Stürmer reported 558 convictions for 1936. After serving their prison sentences, those convicted were automatically sent to concentration camps.

Jewish Self-Assertion

A radical right-wing government, the establishment of a dictatorship, and passage of anti-Jewish laws confronted German Jewry with an unprecedented historical situation. In face of external pressure, various groups differing widely in both politics and religion decided to unite under one umbrella. Conservatives and liberals, assimilated Jews and Zionists jointly founded the "National Association of German Jews" *(Reichsvertretung der deutschen Juden)*. It faced a host of new problems that rapidly multiplied and became more and more difficult to resolve.

During the five years separating Hitler's appointment as Chancellor and the November pogrom of 1938, the ministerial departments and administrative bodies, professional associations and public institutions in the Reich, states and municipalities adopted over 1,200 laws and decrees, directives, guidelines and implementing regulations that increasingly restricted the civil and human rights of the Jews in Germany.

The bases of Jewish existence gradually disappeared as Jews were pushed out of the economic sector and deprived of their livelihoods. This was done initially through expulsion from professions, and subsequently through "Aryanization" (compulsory sale of Jewish property). Between 1933 and 1939, two thirds of all gainfully employed Jews lost their jobs. As early as 1935, one in three people depended on welfare benefits.

A "Central Committee for Aid and Development" was established. It was responsible for organizing economic and social self-help. Branch offices opened throughout Germany to assist the unemployed through counseling, loans, procurement of jobs and vocational retraining. Existing social and cultural institutions had to be expanded, and others created from scratch to help the persecuted reshape their lives. The "Jewish Cultural Association" *(Jüdischer Kulturbund)* was formed. The Jewish press, which prior to 1933 had but a small circulation, found a growing readership. A vast common effort was made to render assistance, reduce hardship, and restore self-esteem and courage to the persecuted.

The emigration of the younger generation had to be launched; at the same time, there was still hope that those unable to emigrate might be allowed to continue a modicum of Jewish life, albeit in isolation from the life of the state and nation. Later, the phrase "carrying on in the face of destruction" *(Aufbau im Untergang)* would be coined, referring to a heroic effort that was ultimately doomed. Yet it remains an impressive testimony to German Jewry's strong will to survive, and its sense of social responsibility.

11. Social Self-Help

From 1933 on, as more and more people became destitute, Jewish welfare and social services faced a workload that grew from year to year. Clinics and day-care centers, orphanages, institutions for the blind and deaf-mute, old-age and nursing homes, all had to be administered. As a result of emigration, the remaining Jewish population became superannunated. The army of the needy increased. In October 1935, the "Jewish Winter Relief" organization was established. It was supported entirely by donations. Money and provisions, clothing and medical supplies were collected and distributed to those in need. Soup kitchens for elderly people without families were established.

Lunchtime at the Jewish Winter Relief organization
(Poster reads: ,Political discussions strictly forbidden")

12. "Kulturbund"

Kulturbund theater on Kommandantenstrasse in Berlin's Kreuzberg district

After 1933, an ever-increasing number of Jews was ousted from professions and jobs. Among those affected were civil servants, judges and lawyers, teachers and professors, physicians and pharmacists. Jewish artists were no longer allowed to perform in public; the founding of the "Jüdische Kulturbund" thus provided them with new job opportunities. It opened in Berlin in October 1933 with a performance of Lessing's "Nathan the Wise," a plea for tolerance.

Theater and opera, concerts and lectures, exhibitions and subsequently movies were offered by subscription. By 1934, the Kulturbund had 20,000 members. From 1938 on, only the works of Jewish authors and composers could be performed. In the fall of 1941, all branches of the Kulturbund in Germany were closed down.

JÜDISCHE WINTERHILFE

KÖLN, Rubensstrasse 33 · Fernsprech-Sammelnummer 21 05 41 · Postsch.-Konto Köln 618

KÖLN, 15. Dezember 1939.

An alle Gemeindemitglieder!

Gross ist die Not

aller derjenigen, die sich täglich an uns wenden, um wenigstens in den kalten Wintermonaten eine zusätzliche Unterstützung zu erhalten.

Das tägliche Brot

fehlt diesen armen Menschen! Was dies bedeutet, weiß mancher sicherlich noch nicht, der unseren Sammler mit einer kleinen Geldspende abfertigt, obwohl selbst große Beträge bestimmt noch kein Opfer für ihn wären.

Gross ist die Not

viel größer als diese Spender sich vorstellen können! Ist es nicht traurig, wenn Mütter nicht wissen, wo sie für ihre Kinder

Das tägliche Brot

hernehmen sollen! Wissen diese Spender, was es heißt, sich in ungeheizten, kalten Räumen aufhalten zu müssen? So

Gross ist die Not

bei hunderten unserer Gemeindemitgliedern, und das ist der Grund, warum wir Sie immer wieder bitten und Ihnen immer wieder zurufen müssen

Jeder Will Helfen **Jedem Wird Hilfe!**

Also nicht nur spenden, sondern **opfern!**

Jüdische Winterhilfe

[Unterschrift]

Nächste Sammlung
Sonntag, den 17. Dezember

13. Schools and Sports Clubs

Student sport festival, Grunewald district of Berlin, 1936

As early as April 1933, a quota system for Jews was introduced into schools and universities. Discrimination became the norm. Existing Jewish schools had to expand their staffs and curricula. By 1936, they were in a position to accept 60 percent of all Jewish pupils. In 1938, all Jews still enrolled in public schools had to leave them.

As Jews became "undesirable" in German sports clubs, municipal athletic fields, and public swimming pools, Jewish sports clubs began to attract many new members. For a few years, until all such Jewish institutions

Rykestrasse primary school, Berlin 1937

were banned in 1938, they provided both a refuge and relief from the oppression of everyday life. Jewish schools organized their own sporting events.

14. Vocational Retraining

Vocational training and Hebrew class, Berlin 1935

Jews were ousted from their chosen occupations in increasing numbers. Thus, in a massive vocational retraining program, unemployed academicians and business employees were taught new skills in handicrafts and agriculture. Those willing to emigrate thereby improved their chances of obtaining an immigration permit and rebuilding a new life abroad. Another program was particularly geared toward youth. In 1936, 80 training centers existed in Germany and elsewhere to prepare young people for life in Palestine. Hebrew language courses constituted an important part of the training. In 1938, one third of the training centers in Germany were destroyed. In 1941, vocational training was banned entirely.

15. Emigration

The Nazi regime did all it could to increase pressure on the Jews to emigrate. But the impoverishment of the German Jews, caused by government policies, and the tax imposed on emigrants proved to be obstacles. Many people were unable to raise the necessary funds. Furthermore, most foreign countries had restricted immigration quotas and refused to admit destitute refugees. Half a million Jews lived in Germany in 1933. Of these, more than 360,000 succeeded in emigrating. Parents frequently sent their children abroad; there were children's transports to England and organized emigration of young people to Palestine. A special train left Berlin on September 2, 1936 carrying 650 youngsters from around Germany to a boat in Marseille.

Berlin, Anhalter railroad station, September 2, 1936

Chronology

1933

January 30	*Hindenburg appoints Hitler Reich Chancellor*
February 27	*Reichstag fire; first wave of arrests*
February 28	*Decree for the Protection of People and State nullifies basic democratic laws*
March 5	*Last elections to the Reichstag; Nazi Party receives 44 percent of the vote*
March 10	*First provisional concentration camps established*
March 22	Racial Hygiene Department established at the Ministry of the Interior. *Dachau concentration camp established.*
March 23	*Reichstag adopts Enabling Act over the opposition of the Social Democrats and in the absence of the arrested Communist block*
March 24	*Communist Party banned*
March 28	*German Catholic episcopate takes oath of allegiance to Hitler*
April 1	Boycott of all Jewish store owners, physicians, pharmacists, and lawyers
April 7	Law for the Restoration of the Professional Civil Service mandates firing of Jews and political opponents
April 16	*Protestant Supreme Church Council of the Old Prussian Union takes oath of allegiance to Hitler*
April 26	*Secret State Police [Gestapo] established*
May 2	*All independent unions banned*
May 10	*Public book burnings. Democratic literature banned.*
June 16	Jewish "Kulturbund" founded
July 14	*Germany becomes a one-party state*
September 17	National Association of German Jews established
September 22	Reich Chamber of Culture Law bans politically and "racially" undesirable writers and artists
October 19	*Germany leaves League of Nations*
November 12	*First Reichstag elections in the one-party state. 92 % of votes go to National Socialists.*

1934

January 26	*Friendship and Nonaggression Pact concluded with Poland*
February 7	*Reich Defense Council resolves to prepare for war on the economic front*
June 30	*"Röhm putsch": Liquidation of "left-wing" SA leadership.*
July 20	*SS becomes an independent organization and takes control of concentration camps from storm troopers*
July 25	*Attempted coup in Vienna: Austria's Chancellor Dollfuss assassinated*
August 2	*With Hindenburg's death, Hitler becomes Head of State and Supreme Commander of the Armed Forces*

1935

January 13	*Saar region votes for return to Germany*
June 18	*Anglo-German fleet treaty*
September 15	Reichstag adopts Nuremberg Racial Laws

1936

March 7	*Occupation and remilitarization of the Rhineland.*
March 29	*Plebiscite: 99 % of the voters approve of Hitler's policies*
July 12	*Sachsenhausen concentration camp established*
July 18	*Fascist military coup against the Spanish Republic; beginning of Spanish Civil War*
August 1	*Olympic summer games open in Berlin*

1937

July 16	*Buchenwald concentration camp established*
September	"Aryanization" of the economy begins, leading to forced sales of Jewish property

2. The Prewar Period

The beginning of the National Socialist regime was marked by the end of government by law, prohibition of all democratic organizations and physical persecution of their adherents, who were murdered, arrested or driven into exile. Within a year, Nazification *[Gleichschaltung]* had been accomplished and all key positions filled with new people. In the summer of 1934, after the death of Hindenburg, Hitler became head of state and supreme commander of the armed forces. From then on, he could rule without restraint.

Dazzled and misinformed by centrally-controlled propaganda, many people believed Nazi promises and adopted their slogans. But even those who were not enthusiastic about the new authorities obeyed their orders almost without exception, even where there was no coercion. In this way they helped shore up the dictatorship. This subservient mentality proved stronger than the spirit of democracy, which never managed to take root in the defeated country after 1918.

Anti-Semitism provided the demagogic formula that seemed to explain all of society's shortcomings. Once the absurd thesis that the Jews were to blame for everything had caught on, it was enough to brand undesirable ideas, people or institutions Jewish to justify any measures taken against them. Thus Marxism, parliamentary democracy, the League of Nations, and social democracy were all labeled Jewish creations. Anti-Semitic slogans thus supplied a justification for everything, from banning modern art and literature to criminalization of democratic parties and labor unions.

Once he had suppressed public criticism of his policies, Hitler turned to the two objectives he had had in mind from the beginning: his campaign against the Jews and his preparations for a war of conquest. The Nuremberg racial laws, which annulled the European Enlightenment concept that all citizens were equal before the law, were merely the beginning. The culmination of this process, for the time being, was the so-called "Reich *Kristallnacht*" in November 1938, a pogrom organized by the state. It was followed by a renewed wave of intensified anti-Jewish laws. Men and women whose families had lived in Germany for centuries were forced to leave their homeland, but only those who fled overseas were truly out of danger.

On January 30, 1939, Hitler threatened in the Reichstag that the outbreak of a war, which he was already planning at the time, would mean the "destruction of the Jewish race in Europe."

1. The Role of the Gestapo

The headquarters of the state and party terror machinery was built in 1933, next door to the center of government. In 1936 they were linked organizationally. Himmler was named "Head of the SS and Chief of the German Police." In 1939, the secret police (Gestapo), criminal investigaton department, and the SS Security Service (SD) joined to form the Reich Security Main Office (RSHA).

Its main task was surveillance of political opponents. The SD also kept files on Jews and Jewish organizations, both domestically and abroad. In 1936 it pushed for "Aryanization" and forced emigration. In 1937 it suggested using the upcoming census of 1939 to begin a file on Jews *(Judenkartei)*. The Gestapo department that dealt with Jews drafted anti-Jewish laws, in close cooperation with the corresponding departments of the Ministry of the Interior and the Justice Ministry.

2. Annexation of Austria ("Anschluss")

On March 12, 1938, the German Army marched into Austria. In its wake came Himmler, Heydrich, Eichmann, and 20,000 mobile policemen. In a lightning operation, some 50,000 political opponents were arrested. On the night after the invasion, Austrian storm troopers in Vienna began looting Jewish businesses and apartments. German anti-Jewish laws were introduced in Austria as well.

3. Vienna, March 1938

Jewish citizens forced to clean streets

■ *"Unfortunately, Party members have misbehaved on a large scale during the past few days, in a thoroughly undisciplined manner. I have announced in the press today that Communist party-liners, wearing [Nazi] Party uniforms, have tried to endanger public order and security by illegally seizing property, searching homes, and making arrests."*
Reinhard Heydrich, March 17, 1938

▲ *"The pogrom-like excesses in the streets of Vienna were a popular form of 'entertainment' in these days. Accompanied by howling mobs, groups of Jews were forced to wash Schuschnigg's election slogans off the pavements and walls. Other Jews, provided with brushes and paint, were forced to mark Jewish stores with the word 'Jew' or with a Star of David."*
Report by J. Moser

4. Expulsion to Poland

During the night of October 28, 1938, 17,000 Jews of Polish extraction from Germany, Austria and the "Sudetenland" were arrested before being expelled. Guarded by police and SS, they were then taken in trains to the Polish border. Many of them had become German citizens after 1918. Polish authorities allowed approximately 10,000 into their country.

Nuremberg, October 28, 1938

The rest remained in a no-man's land near the border town of Zbaszyn, which at the time had only 4,000 inhabitants. There, the majority of the expellees lived in unheated stables and barracks until August 1939. Altogether, 32,000 Polish Jews were expelled from the German Reich prior to the outbreak of war. It was a dress rehearsal for subsequent deportations.

5. The November Pogrom

■ *"1) In a short period of time, operations against the Jews, especially against synagogues, will take place throughout Germany. They are not to be interrupted; however, in cooperation with the police, it is to be ensured that plundering and other types of incidents can be prohibited.*
2) Where important archival material is located in synagogues, it is to be taken into possession through immediate action.
3) The arrest of 20 to 30,000 Jews in the Reich is to be prepared for. Mainly wealthy Jews should be selected. More precise instructions will be issued in the course of the night.

Synagogue in Euskirchen

4) Should Jews in possession of weapons be encountered during the operations, the strictest measures should be applied. SS special troops and general SS may be deployed in the operations. In any event, state police leadership of the operations must be ensured through appropriate measures. Plundering, theft, etc. are to be prevented at all costs."

Secret Gestapo telex, November 9, 1938

6. "Reich *Kristallnacht*"

Euskirchen

When a young Jew shot a German diplomat in Paris after his parents were expelled to Poland, he provided the pretext for a pogrom not seen in Germany for centuries. Although publicly portrayed as "spontaneous protest," it was in fact an operation organized by the Nazi party. Throughout Germany, storm troopers and SS in civilian clothing set fire to synangogues and destroyed Jewish businesses. During that night, arson and destruction of property, looting and rape, murder and homicide went unpunished. The police stood by and watched. The fire department intervened only when fire endangered other buildings.

7. Mass Arrests

267 synagogues and roughly a thousand prayer halls were destroyed, 7,500 stores and offices devastated, 91 human beings slain. Neither the number of the seriously injured who ultimately died from their mistreatment, nor the number of suicides, is known.

The victims, not the perpetrators, were arrested. 26,000 Jews between the ages of 16 and 60 were taken to the concentration camps Dachau, Buchenwald, and Sachsenhausen and held until they could either buy their freedom or emigrate.

Baden-Baden

8. Conference in Göring's Ministry

On November 12, 1938, a meeting was held in the Reich Aviation Ministry, presided over by Göring. Here, further measures were taken to deprive German Jews of their rights. Expropriations, compulsory sales, emigration were to be stepped up. The victims of the pogrom were forc-

Berliner
Lokal-Anzeiger

Göring verordnet: Eine Milliarde Sühneleistung der Juden in Deutschland

Verordnungen zur Lösung der Judenfrage – Ausschaltung aus dem Wirtschaftsleben
Wiederherstellung aller Schäden – Weitere Maßnahmen in Kürze zu erwarten

ed to bear the costs of the damage done them; they had collectively to pay the German government a billion marks by way of "reparations."

- *"Oppose the disgrace of the anti-Jewish pogroms!*
Faithful to the tradition of the German workers' movement, in the true spirit of the greatest German poets and thinkers, the German Communist Party raises its voice against Hitler's anti-Jewish pogroms, which have cast the deepest disgrace on Germany's honor before all humanity....
Solidarity in sympathy and aid to our Jewish fellow citizens, solidarity with the persecuted Communists and Socialists, solidarity with the threatened Catholics, solidarity among us all in the daily fight to subvert and overthrow the Nazi regime by creating the broadest possible German popular front movement -- that is what the hour demands of all peace and freedom-loving Germans!
Unity makes us strong. Unity will bring victory! Down with the Hitler dictatorship! Long live peace! Long live freedom!"
From a declaration by the Central Committee of the KPD. Die Rote Fahne, no. 7 (special edition), November 1938.

- *"I shall choose the wording that the German Jews in their entirety will be saddled with a contribution of one billion (marks) by way of punishment for their reprehensible crimes, etc. etc. That'll hit home. Those swine won't commit another murder for a while. By the way, I am telling you again: I would not like to be a Jew in Germany."*
Hermann Göring on November 12, 1938

9. Deprivation of Rights by Law

Long before the pogrom of 1938, anti-Jewish measures had increased month by month. Jews had to report their financial assets; their businesses had to be registered and specially marked; Jewish tenants no longer enjoyed legal protection; physicians and lawyers were forbidden to practice; an additional given name, either Israel or Sarah, became compulsory; and passports were marked

Berlin

10. Escape from Germany

The terror of the pogrom, the mass arrests, and the wave of new discriminatory laws created increased pressure to emigrate. After November 9, 1938, emigration turned into mass flight. In less than a year prior to the outbreak of war, more people had left the country than during the entire preceding five years.

Anyone who could get an entry visa and ship's passage fled overseas. All others seeking refuge in one of the neighboring European countries were ultimately caught by their persecutors during the years to come. Safety could be found only in Sweden, Switzerland, and Great Britain.

with a "J." These were only a few of the numerous directives.

New decrees followed in rapid succession. All Jewish businesses and workshops were closed. Jews were no longer permitted to enter public parks, attend cultural events, or keep pets. Their children were expelled from public schools and universities. Jews had to hand over their radios and jewelry and were forbidden to go out on the streets after 8 p.m.

11. Destination: England

For refugees from Germany, the British Isles provided a safe haven. Jewish committees helped the new arrivals with registration formalities and in the search for work. Once war

broke out, nearly all the men were interned as "enemy aliens," and many were deported to Canada.

Nearly 10,000 children reached England in group transports. From then on they grew up in strange families. Most never again saw their parents, who had remained behind in Germany. Altogether, 55,000 refugees found asylum in England.

12.

▲ *"Finally in England -- a tired little refugee, who arrived in Harwich this morning."*
"The first German refugee children arrive: 2,000 boys and girls between 5 and 17 years old, the first group of 5,000 Jewish refugee children from Germany, arrived in Harwich this morning. They were brought to the Dovercourt Bay reception camp."
Press text on the back of the photo (Fox)

Harwich, England, December 2, 1938

13. To Shanghai and Palestine

Off the coast of Palestine

Many Jews tried to escape to Palestine or South America on chartered steamships. But not all ships reached their destinations. Some were turned back; others were shipwrecked before reaching the safety of the coast. The stories of the "St. Louis," headed for Cuba, and the sinking of the "Struma" in the Sea of Marmara became known throughout the world.

The only place of refuge which did not restrict emigration before October 1939 was Shanghai. 14,000 refugees, most from Germany, arrived there prior to the outbreak of war. Their number increased to 17,000 by 1941. 90 percent were Jews. Only a few found work. From 1943 to 1945, the Japanese occupation forces interned them all.

Chronology

1938

March 13	*"Anschluss" of Austria*
March 28	All Jewish congregations in Germany, hitherto corporate bodies under public law, become private associations
April 22	Decree prohibiting the "camouflaging of Jewish businesses"
April 26	Decree on registration of Jewish financial assets. First step toward elimination of Jews from the economic sector
June 15	"Operation Asocials": Arrest of all Jews with previous convictions, including those with mere traffic violations. 1,500 persons sent to concentration camps
July 6	Evian Conference on Jewish emigration from Germany
August	Establishment of the "Central Office for Jewish Emigration" in Vienna
August 17	Decree forcing Jews to adopt the additional names of Sarah and Israel, respectively, as of January 1, 1939
September 29	*Munich Conference. Annexation of the "Sudetenland"*
October 5	Jewish passports marked with a "J"
October 14	Conference at Göring's ministry on "Aryanization" of the economy
October 28	17,000 Jews expelled to Poland
November 7	Herschel Grynszpan, whose parents were among those expelled, shoots Ernst vom Rath, member of the German embassy in Paris
November 9	"Reich *Kristallnacht*": state-organised pogrom against the Jews
November 12	Göring Conference imposes a "Punitive Payment" on the German Jews for damages suffered, amounting to one billion Reichsmark. It resolves to close all Jewish businesses and workshops and exclude Jews from all cultural events
November 15	Jewish children excluded from public schools

1939

January	Dissolution of all Jewish political organisations, including the Zionist Organisation of Germany and the Central Association of German Citizens of Jewish Faith (CV)
January 17	Tenant protection annulled for Jews. Jewish dentists, veterinarians, apothecaries, nonmedical practitioners and nurses barred from practising their profession
January 24	Founding of the "Reich Center for Jewish Emigration," with branch offices in Vienna and Prague
January 30	Hitler announces in the Reichstag that war -- which he was already planning -- would mean "the destruction of the Jewish race in Europe"
March 15	*German troops occupy Czechoslovakia. "Protectorate of Bohemia and Moravia" formed*
March 23	*German troops march into Memel Territory*
May 18	"Der Stürmer" calls for slaughter of all Jews in the Soviet Union
July 20	British Government orders ban on Jewish emigration to Palestine
July 26	Eichmann takes over the Prague Central Office of the Emigration Office
August 23	*Nonaggression pact signed by Germany and the Soviet Union*
September 1	*German invasion of Poland; beginning of the Second World War*

3. War against Poland

The decision, for which the groundwork had been laid the year before with the Munich Accord, came in early fall of 1939. Although Hitler had meanwhile violated the agreement when the German army invaded Czechoslovakia, negotiations between the Soviet Union and the western powers on joint guarantees for Poland came to naught. Shortly thereafter, and to the surprise of the world, the irreconcilable enemies in Moscow and Berlin concluded a non-aggression pact. In an additional secret clause, they divided their respective spheres of interest in eastern Europe. Stalin believed he had averted the danger of a German attack, at least for the moment. Germany was now free to invade Poland without risking a conflict with the Soviet Union.

Hitler started the war on September 1. He had been systematically preparing for it since 1934 by intensive rearmament and militarization of the entire society. The attack on Poland was the first step in a projected conquest of living space [Lebensraum] in eastern Europe. The decisive second step followed barely two years later with the invasion of the Soviet Union.

Poland was vanquished in less than four weeks. The Soviet Union occupied the western regions of White Russia and the Ukraine, which it had been forced to hand over to Poland in 1920, and subjected them to its system of rule. Germany annexed the western Polish provinces. Central Poland was placed under German occupation law and declared the socalled Generalgouvernement. Of the three and a half million Jews in Poland, two million fell into German hands, while more than a quarter million fled to the Soviet Russian side.

German rule in Poland was extremely brutal. All manner of repressive measures hit the nation hard: shooting of hostages, persecution of intellectuals, preventive mass arrests of potential enemies and their internment in concentration camps, deportation of hundreds of thousands for forced labor in Germany, and economic pillage of the country for the German war effort.

Far worse was the fate that awaited the Jewish population. The violent terror, torments, lootings, and pogroms of the initial weeks were followed by an administrative war. The laws and regulations, were, for the most part, already familiar in Germany: all Jews and their places of business had to be specially marked, and they had to register all their possessions. Forced labor was introduced, as were the ban on residing in certain districts and exclusion from public transportation. Bank accounts were blocked, property "Aryanized" or placed into receivership. A year after the German invasion, "resettlement" into ghettos began.

1. Surprise Attack

September 1, 1939

■ *"It is not our tast to Germanize the East in the traditional sense – that is, to teach the people there the German language and German laws – but to ensure that only people with truly German, Teutonic blood live in the East."*

The Reichsführer SS, Heinrich Himmler

2. Invasion of Warsaw

On September 1, 1939, the German Army invaded Poland. Warsaw capitulated one month later. Jewish men were immediately drafted to clear away the rubble. In many places, Heydrich's Special Units instigated pogroms in order to justify and lay the psychological groundwork for anti-Jewish legislation.

Warsaw, September 1939

3. Tripartition of Poland

(see map, next page)

4. Humiliation

Poland, October 1939

5. Ridicule

Police and rabbi

Tripartition of Poland

Poland was divided into three parts. The eastern territories beyond the Curzon Line, which had belonged to Russia until 1921, reverted to the Soviet Union, while the western Polish provinces became part of the German Reich. The remainder became the so-called Generalgouvernement.

6. Terror

Lodz

7. Distinguishing Markings

The first town in Europe where the medieval marking of Jews with a yellow patch was reintroduced was Wloclawek. In Cracow, a yellow star had to be worn on the breast and back.

In November 1939, a white armband with a blue Star of David was introduced throughout the *Generalgouvernement*. Jewish property had already been registered and confiscated in September.

8. "Registration"

(see poster, next page, translation as following)

**Decree
of November 14, 1939**

Considerable disturbances caused by the Jews in the public life of the area administered by the governor of Kalisch lead me to require the following for the area administered by the governor of Kalisch:

§ 1
Regardless of age or sex, Jews will wear as a special marking a 10 cm. wide armband of Jewish yellow on their upper arms, immediately below the underarm.

§ 2
In the area administered by the governor of Kalisch, Jews will not be allowed to leave their homes between 5 p.m. and 8 a.m. without a special permit.

§ 3
Violations of this decree will be punishable by death. If mitigating circumstances are present, an unlimited fine or imprisonment, separately or in conjunction, may be imposed.

Lodz, November 14, 1939

The Governor of Kalisch
Uebelhoer

Verordnung

vom 14. November 1939

Erhebliche durch die Juden verursachte Mißstände im öffentlichen Leben des Verwaltungsbereichs des Regierungspräsidenten zu Kalisch veranlassen mich, für den Verwaltungsbereich des Regierungspräsidenten zu Kalisch folgendes zu bestimmen:

§ 1

Als besonderes Kennzeichen tragen Juden ohne Rücksicht auf Alter und Geschlecht am rechten Oberarm unmittelbar unter der Achselhöhle eine 10 cm breite Armbinde in judengelber Farbe.

§ 2

Juden dürfen im Verwaltungsbereich des Regierungspräsidenten zu Kalisch in der Zeit von 17—8 Uhr ihre Wohnung ohne meine besondere Genehmigung nicht verlassen.

§ 3

Zuwiderhandlungen gegen diese Verordnung werden mit dem Tode bestraft. Bei Vorliegen mildernder Umstände kann auf Geldstrafe in unbeschränkter Höhe oder Gefängnis, allein oder in Verbindung miteinander, erkannt werden.

§ 4

Diese Verordnung tritt bis auf die Bestimmung in § 1 sofort, § 1 vom 18. November 1939 ab in Kraft.

Lodz, den 14. November 1939.

Der Regierungspräsident zu Kalisch

Uebelhoer

9. Deprivation of Rights

■ *"Annonncement of Registration of Jews for forced labor"*

"By decree of October 26, 1939, a work requirement was introduced for Jews residing in the General-gouvernment, to take immediate effect. To implement this decree, I order the following:

*§ 1
All male Jews from the ages of 12 to 60 are to report immediately to the Jewish council connected to the office of the mayor of the responsible source community for the purpose of registration. The responsiblity of the Jewish council extends to the entire area of the source community. Baptized Jews are also subject to registration. ...*

*§ 5
Up to 10 years' imprisonment may be imposed on any Jew eligible for forced labor:*

a) who does not report immediately to the responsible Jewish council for registration,
b) who supplies false or incomplete information about himself,
c) who pretends inability or reduced capacity to work,
d) who disposes of the tools of his trade."

Announcement by the District Head of Sanok, Dr. Schaar, March 7, 1940

10. Punitive Action in Olkusz

To intimidate the population and discourage any form of resistance, the German occupying forces demonstrated their power at every opportunity. When a German policeman was killed by a burglar in the town of Olkusz in July 1940, the police and the army carried out a punitive operation. All the men, Jewish and Gentile, were arrested and rounded up on the market square.
With hands tied behind their backs and faces to the ground, they were forced to lie on the pavement for an entire day, while being kicked and beaten with rifle butts. Twenty men were publicly executed as hostages. The number of hostages was later raised in all the occupied countries to 100 for each German killed and 50 for each one wounded.

11. "Resettlement"

"Resettlement" was a continuous process. Through compulsory resettlement, Jews were moved from the Warta region to Lodz or the General-gouvernement, from villages to the nearest town, from small towns to larger ones, and within the towns into special "Jewish residential districts" -- that is, ghettos that were subsequently sealed off and surrounded by armed guards. A year later, the small ghettos were again dissolved and their inhabitants to the ghetto of the nearest city, to a work camp, or directly to an extermination camp.

12.

Arrival in the Lodz Ghetto

13. En Route to the Ghetto

Warsaw

▲ *"The Jews in the numerous small towns were assembled, and the open countryside purged of Jewish families residing there ... The people moved silently through the bitterly cold night, a picture of pain and suffering. In Lodz proper, Jews from all over, carrying only hand luggage, also moved silently for an entire week to the central ghetto, which a quarter of a million people had been assigned as their residence. And it was once again on a nasty winter's night that special detachments combed through Jewish homes for possible stragglers. Anyone who did not immediately leave his home was shot on the spot."*
Report by Pastor G. Schedler, Lodz

14.

Lodz Ghetto

Chronology

1939

September 1	*German attack on Poland*
September 2	*Camp Stutthof near Danzig established*
September 3	*Great Britain and France declare war on Germany*
Sept. 1 to 21	"Special Units" of Security Police and Security Service organise mass arrests and shootings of hostages among the Polish and Jewish population as well as numerous pogroms
September 17	*Occupation of East Poland by the Soviet Union*
September 21	Heydrich orders the Security Police to concentrate Jewish populations in the larger towns, have them form councils of elders, initiate a census of Jews, and prepare a survey of all economically significant Jewish businesses
September 27	*Warsaw capitulates*
October 7	*The four western Polish provinces are incorporated into the German Reich. Central Poland becomes German-occupied territory (the "Generalgouvernement")*
October 12–27	First deportation of Jews from Austria and Moravia to Poland
October 16	*Cracow becomes capital of the Generalgouvernement*
October 18	*Resettlement of ethnic Germans from the Baltic states to the annexed western Polish provinces begins. Hans Frank appointed Governor General*
October 26	Forced labor for all Jews between the ages of 14 and 60 in the *Generalgouvernement*
October 28	First introduction of a yellow badge in Wloclawek
November 8	*Attempt on Hitler's life in Munich*
November 12	Beginning of deportations of Jews and Poles from the western provinces to the Generalgouvernement
November 14	Jews in the Warta region forced to wear distinguishing marks Formation
November 28	Jewish Councils in the Generalgouvernement ordered
December 1	Introduction of the Jewish star in the Generalgouvernement
December 5	Confiscation of all Jewish property in Poland
December	All Jewish communities in places with less than 500 inhabitants dissolved. Resettlement of the Jewish population into special "residential districts," later turned into ghettos, begins

4. The Ghettos

In 1940, ghettos were established everywhere in occupied Poland by order of the German administration. Poorer city districts, already inhabited predominantly by Jews, were proclaimed "Jewish residential districts." All Jews had to move into them, while everyone else had to leave. Once the "resettlement" had been concluded, the ghetto was sealed off by police and enclosed behind a fence or wall. Anyone who tried to leave could be condemned to death or shot on the spot by guards. The two largest ghettos were in Lodz (Litzmannstadt) in the annexed Warta region (160,000 inhabitants), and in Warsaw in the *Generalgouvernement* (450,000 inhabitants).

The Jewish Councils *[Judenräte]* tried in vain to organize functioning community life and ensure a food supply. Both were under the authority of the German civilian administration, which was controlled in turn by the Gestapo. The ghettos were not in a position to maintain themselves on their own. Where German businesses were established because of the available cheap labor, as in Warsaw, they employed only a minority of Jews. Smuggling, carried out at the risk of one's life, became vital. In Lodz, where everybody had to work, but smuggling was impossible, hunger was also prevalent. Poverty spread, and social contrasts became more pronounced. Courageous individuals attempted to maintain their humanity and that of others through social and cultural endeavours, but the general decline continued unabated.

Isolation from the outside world and insufficient provisions led to escalating pauperization of the ghetto populations. Overcrowded housing, continuous undernourishment, and disastrous sanitary conditions caused numerous deaths. In Warsaw alone, 96,000 people died in the ghetto.

In January 1942, the SS began deportations to extermination camps. The "evacuations" began in the Warta region and continued in mid-March in the *Generalgouvernement*. Shelters for the homeless, prisons, hospitals, homes for the aged, and children's homes were emptied first. On July 22, it was Warsaw's turn. At first, attempts were made to lure the starved people with promises of bread and jam. Soon brute force had to be employed to round up the terrified people to fill the mandatory daily quota of 5,000 victims.

After a week, the Jewish auxiliary police was replaced by SS volunteers. These launched a barbaric manhunt, clearing street by street and block by block. Everyone without work was taken away--and that meant the vast majority. A wild struggle ensued to obtain life-saving employment certificates, but very soon they too became invalid. 310,000 people were deported from Warsaw by September 1942. Only people working in firms deemed essential to the war effort were spared for the time being, as were their families.

1.

■ *"In accordance with the decree of Sept. 13, 1940, relating to restricted residence in the Generalgouvernment, a Jewish residential district will be established in the City of Warsaw. Jews now residing in or moving to the City of Warsaw will be required to live there."*

Dr. Fischer, Chief of the Warsaw District, October 2, 1940

Warsaw Ghetto

■ *"The establishment of the ghetto is obviously only a temporary measure. At which juncture and by what means the ghetto, and with it the City of Lodz, will be purged of Jews, I shall ultimately decide. In any case, the final objective must be the total elimination of this pestilence."*

Directive by the Kalisz District President, Friedrich Uebelhör, dated December 10, 1939

2. At the Ghetto Gates

■ *"The Jewish residential district is separated from the rest of the city by existing fire walls and dividing walls, and by bricked up street blocks, windows, doors, and construction sites. Walls are three meters in height, topped by an additional meter of barbed wire. In addition, everything is closely guarded by motorized and mounted police patrols."*

The Chief of Resettlement in Warsaw, Waldemar Schön, dated January 20, 1941

3.

Warsaw Ghetto

4. Street Scenes

Warsaw Ghetto

■ *"Those slandering foreign journalists who so often write such drivel about alleged barbaric persecutions of Jews in the German East would be well advised to observe in person how generously the German administration allows the Jews to continue their own way of life."*

Dr. Max Freiherr du Prel, 1942

5. Attempts to Survive

Street collections, Warsaw Ghetto

The Jewish Social Self-Help association organized street collections to assist the poorest of the poor. It also established soup kitchens. By the summer of 1941, 120,000 human beings relied on the watery soup dispensed there daily as their only meal.

The ghetto dwellers tried as long as possible to preserve their dignity. Despite mounting material hardships, theater performances and concerts took place even in the most modest of circumstances. Books became precious treasures.

6. Work as a Privilege

Warsaw

Under existing conditions, even twelve hours of work in a factory proved to be a privilege. In the Warsaw Ghetto, German firms provided only enough work for some ten thousand people. The overwhelming majority remained unemployed. A few operated primitive workshops. Others tried street peddling, selling personal belongings, or begging. In Lodz, where forced labor prevailed, many were also starving.

■ *"For more than a year now, food rations have been below the levels granted to convicts. Given the amount of food they receive, no one can contend that in the long run the ghetto dwellers will remain fit for work... The clearest evidence of what the food situation is like is the rapidly mounting mortality rate."*

Amtsleiter Biebow, Ghetto Administration of Lodz, March 4, 1942

Family of beggars, Warsaw

two shots. Type of firearm: carbine '98. Ammunition expended: two rounds."

Private First Class Naumann, Litzmannstadt (Lodz), December 1, 1941

7.

Working permit, Ghetto Lodz

9. Mass Quarters

In 1941, 410,000 people lived in the Warsaw Ghetto, an area of barely four square kilometers. Six to seven people shared a room. As the small communities in the provinces were dissolved, additional tens of thousands were crammed into the overcrowded ghetto.

8. An Ordinary Day in the Ghetto

■ *"On December 1, 1941, between 2 and 4 p.m., I was standing guard at Post No. 4 on Holsteiner Strasse. At 3 p.m., I saw a Jewess climb a ghetto fence and stick her head through the fence, trying to steal turnips off a passing wagon. I made use of my firearm. The Jewess was killed with*

Unpublished news film from Warsaw

Plundered and completely destitute, they vegetated in primitive mass shelters or lived on the street, adding to the army of beggars. They were the first to succumb to hunger and disease.

10.

Unpublished news film from Warsaw

hard to believe -- children are brought to the hospital after being hit... Children also climb over the walls; but that must be done very quickly, because the guard may turn around just then. If he sees what is happening, he will fire at once."

Diary of Prof. Ludwik Hirszfeld, Warsaw

11. Children as Smugglers

Children still too young to wear an armband with the star of David were usually best suited to smuggling food into the ghetto. If caught by the police, they could be shot to death. The beets and potatoes intended for entire families were confiscated. Other children who were still too small or already too weak, among them many homeless children, became beggars.

● *"Not all German guards are murderers and executioners, but unfortunately too many of them reach for their weapons too quickly and fire on the children. Day after day -- it is*

12.

■ *"Gentlemen, I must ask you to banish all sentiments of compassion. We must exterminate the Jews wherever we encounter them...*

In the Generalgouvernment we have an estimated 2.5 million; counting those of partly Jewish blood with their kit and caboodle, we now have perhaps 3.5 million Jews.

Those 3.5 million Jews we cannot shoot, nor can we poison them; however, we shall manage to take steps that will somehow lead to their successful extermination, in connection with the extensive measures planned in the Reich that remain to be discussed."

Governor General Hans Frank on
September 9, 1941

13. Death in the Street

Unpublished news film from Warsaw

No one could live long if he or she was homeless. Many beggars starved or froze to death in the streets. Every day, the corpses were collected and loaded on carts. Because most families had no money to pay for a funeral, they also placed their dead on the sidewalks. The bodies were often naked and covered only in newspaper, as cloth was too precious. Even before the deportations began in summer 1942, 96,000 people had died in the Warsaw Ghetto alone.

■ *"The rapid increase in the number of deaths during May of this year shows that lack of food has already led to famine... The following figures give a striking picture of the death rate:*

January '41:	*898*	*May '41:*	*3,821*
February '41:	*1,023*	*June '41:*	*4,290*
March '41:	*1,608*	*July '41:*	*5,550*
April '41:	*2,061*	*August '41:*	*5,560*

A second reason for the increasing death toll is the appearance of epidemic typhus in the Jewish district."

Ghetto Commissioner Heinz Auerswald on
September 26, 1941

14. 1942 -- A Fateful Year

In summer 1941, Jewish doctors estimated how long it would take before the ghetto had died out, if the miserable conditions continued. They could not yet guess that the second stage of extermination would begin one year later, in which that death through hunger would be replaced by death through gas.

Bekanntmachung Nr. 355.

Betr.:

AUSSIEDLUNG

aus Litzmannstadt-Getto

Hiermit fordere ich die zur Aussiedlung bestimmten Personen auf, sich **unbedingt pünktlich** zu der ihnen bekanntgegebenen Zeit am Sammelpunkt zu stellen.

Diejenigen, die sich nicht freiwillig stellen, werden **zwangsweise geholt,** auch wenn sie sich nicht in ihrer eigenen Wohnung aufhalten, da sie überall gefunden werden.

Bei dieser Gelegenheit beziehe ich mich auf meine Bekanntmachung Nr. 347 v. 30. 12. 1941

und warne die Gettobevölkerung letztmalig,

Personen, die in ihren Wohnungen nicht gemeldet sind, bei sich aufzunehmen und übernachten zu lassen.

Sollten sich für die Aussiedlung bestimmte Personen bei anderen Familien aufhalten, um sich dadurch der Aussiedlung zu entziehen, werden nicht nur die zur Aussiedlung bestimmten Personen, sondern auch die Familien, die diese Personen aufgenommen haben, sowie die Hauswächter der betreffenden Häuser zwangsweise ausgesiedelt.

Dieses ist meine LETZTE WARNUNG!

Litzmannstadt-Getto,
den 14. Januar 1942.

(-) CH. RUMKOWSKI
Der Aelteste der Juden in Litzmannstadt

Notice No. 355

Re.: **Resettlement**
from the Litzmannstadt Ghetto

I hereby order the persons designated for resettlement to appear <u>punctually without fail</u> at the collection point at the time of which they have been informed.
Those who do not appear voluntarily will be <u>forcibly taken</u>, even if they do not remain in their own homes, as they will be found wherever they are.
I take this opportunity to refer to my notice no. 347 of Dec. 30, 1941 and warn the ghetto population for the last time against taking in persons not registered in their dwellings and allowing them to remain overnight.
Should persons designated for resettlement be living with other families in order to avoid resettlement, not only the persons designated for resettlement, but also the families who sheltered these persons, as well as the building watchers of the buildings involved, will be <u>forcibly resettled</u>.

This is my LAST WARNING!

Litzmannstadt Ghetto
14 January 1942

Ch. Rumkowski
Elder of the Jews of Litzmannstadt

15. Bread as Bait

AUFRUF

Ich gebe hiermit bekannt, dass alle Personen, die, gemäss der Anordnung der Behörden zur Aussiedlung kommen, sich am **29., 30.** und **31.** Juli ds. Jhrs. freiwillig zur Abreise melden werden, erhalten pro Person 3 Kg. Brot und 1 Kg. Marmelade.

Sammelpunkt und Produktenverteilung — Stawkiplatz Ecke Wildstrasse.

Der Leiter des Jüdischen Ordnungsdienstes

Warschau, den 29. Juli 1942

Notice

I hereby announce that all persons voluntarily reporting for departure on July 29, 30 and 31 of this year according to the official Decree on Resettlement will receive 3 kg. of bread and 1 kg. of jam per person.

Gathering point and distribution of goods -- Stawkiplatz, corner Wildstrasse.

Warsaw, July 29, 1942   The head of the Jewish Police

---

16. "Evacuation"

Lodz, September 1942

■ *"The evacuation of old, weak, ailing persons over 65, of sick, ailing persons regardless of age, and of children below the age of 10 was scheduled to begin on September 7, 1942. Assisted by Jewish police forces, entire blocks were sealed off without warning by evacuation officials (Secret State Police). The evacuation process lasted through September 12, 1942. Approximately 18,000 persons, adults and children, were affected by it."*

Ghetto Commissariat Litzmannstadt (Lodz) to the Inspector of Security Police (Sipo) and Security Service (SD) on September 24, 1942

17.

■ *"Annonncement:*

1) Beginning on September 5, 1942, evacuation of Jews will be carried out in the Sanok district.

2) Any person who jeopardizes or obstructs the evacuation in any way whatsoever, or assists in such actions, will be shot.

3) Any person who shelters or hides a Jew during or after the evacuation will be shot.

4) Any person who enters the premises of an evacuated Jew without authorization will be shot for looting."

Public announcement by the Higher SS and Police Leader of the Cracow District on September 4, 1942

After the deportation, Warsaw

18. To Chelmno and Treblinka

"Evacuation Police," Lodz

● *"A family that a few minutes earlier had been sitting peacefully at the table suddenly disappeared, as if by ill fortune. I know many instances where somebody who had been absent for just a short while found nobody at home when he returned, neither his wife, his children, nor his elderly parents.*

When the prescribed daily quota of victims had been filled, the operation was suspended, only to be resumed the following morning at dawn."

Michel Mazor, member of the Jewish Self-Help association in the Warsaw Ghetto

Chronology

1940

February 8	Resettlement begins to the „Jewish district" of Lodz
April 11	Lodz renamed Litzmannstadt
April 30	The Lodz Ghetto with 160,000 people sealed off
October 1	Hans Frank orders establishment of ghettos throughout the entire Generalgouvernement
October 2	Order to establish a ghetto in Warsaw
November 15	Warsaw Ghetto is sealed off

1941

January	Famine in the Lodz Ghetto. First strikes and demonstrations
February	72,000 Jews from the provinces deported to the Warsaw Ghetto by April
October 18	Deportations from Germany begin. 20,000 Jews from Berlin, Frankfurt, Düsseldorf, Hamburg, as well as Vienna and Luxembourg, are deported to Lodz by November 3
November 5	5,000 persons, over half of them children, are deported to the "Gypsy camp" of the Lodz Ghetto
December 7	Beginning of mass killings in gas vans at the extermination camp Kulmhof (Chelmno)
December 24	All fur coats confiscated for the German Army

1942

January 12	Survivors of the "Gypsy camp" at Lodz gassed at Chelmno
January 16	Deportations from Lodz to Chelmno. By the end of May, 55,000 people have been gassed, among them 10,000 from Germany
January 20	Wannsee Conference
March 16	Beginning of systematic extermination in the Generalgouvernement ("Operation Reinhard")
March 17–21	26,000 deported from Lublin to Belzec
March 19	15,000 from Lemberg (Lvov) deported to Belzec
May 18	Sobibor Extermination Camp set up
May 28–June 6	6,000 people from Cracow deported to Belzec
June 11–18	13,500 deported from Tarnow to Belzec
July 22	Deportations from the Warsaw Ghetto begin
August 5	6,000 deported from Radom to Treblinka
August 10–23	50,000 deported from Lemberg (Lvov) to Belzec
August 12–18	5,000 people deported from Bedzin and 8,000 from Sosnowiec to Auschwitz
August 16–18	18,000 people from Radom deported to Treblinka. 1,500 shot during evacuation
August 20–24	18,000 people deported from Kielce to Treblinka
Sept. 7–12	16,000 elderly people, invalids, and children under 10 deported from Lodz to Chelmno
September 8	8,000 deported from Tarnow to Belzec
October 3	First major "resettlement" from the Warsaw Ghetto completed: 310,000 people deported to Treblinka and Belzec
October 13–21	20,000 deported from Piotrkow Trybunalski to Treblinka. 500 escape into the woods
October 27–28	7,000 people deported from Cracow to Belzec. 600 shot during evacuation.

5. Mass Executions

On June 22, 1941, Hitler's armies invaded the Soviet Union. This marked the beginning of an unprecedented war of conquest and annihilation that led to the death of more than 27 million citizens of the Soviet Union. For European Jewry, it also meant the beginning of genocide. Here the blueprint for extermination was translated into action at once and on the spot.

In every town captured by German troops, units of the Security Police and Security Service (SD) staged bloody pogroms. Then the military administration issued orders requiring all Jews to register and wear distinguishing badges. Mass shootings usually began a few days or weeks after the troops had arrived. Placards were posted ordering Jews to report for "resettlement." They were then rounded up and either marched or transported on trucks to the outskirts of town. Communists and partisans, Gypsies and the mentally ill shared the same fate.

The firing squads waited at a ravine or anti-tank ditch, originally dug to defend against the German invasion. Watches, wedding rings, and cash were collected in water buckets. Sometimes the victims were forced to dig their own graves. They were then forced to undress and either step to the edge of the pit to be shot, or step into the pit, lie down on top of the layer of bodies already dead, and there receive the bullet.

Four "Special Units" *(Einsatzgruppen)* under the Chief of Security Police and Security Service followed in the wake of the advancing troops and systematically combed the conquered territories of the Soviet Union from the Baltic to the Black Sea. Special Unit A operated in the Baltic republics and the Leningrad district, Unit B in White Russia and the Moscow region, Unit C in the Ukraine, and Unit D in the southern Ukraine, the Crimea and the Caucasus. Their 18 special task forces and separate commandos were reinforced by local auxiliaries. Individual members, as well as entire police and army units, participated in the massacres.

After formation of the "Reich Commissariat for the Eastern Territory" and the "Reich Commissariat for the Ukraine," local SS and police commanders took over the bloody work from the Special Units. From November of 1941 on, gassing trucks were also utilized.

Wherever the army needed manpower, people still able to perform work were spared for the time being. In Vilna, Kovno, Riga, Minsk, and other cities of the Soviet Union, ghettos continued to exist until the summer of 1943. Thereafter, their inmates were also shot or deported to the Sobibor extermination camp.

1. June 22, 1941

■ *"We are finally concluding the colonial and trade policies of the prewar era and will switch to a future territorial policy. But when we talk today in Europe of new land, we are thinking first of all exclusively of Russia and the border states under her control."*

Adolf Hitler, Mein Kampf, Munich, 1925

■ *"The war against Russia is a significant stage in the German people's struggle for existence. It is the old struggle of the Germanic peoples against the Slavs, the defense of European culture against Moscovite-Asiatic deluges, the resistance to Jewish Bolshevism."*

Enclosure No. 2 of the military deployment order to the German Army, May 2, 1941

2. Pogrom in Kovno

■ *"Efforts to carry out purges on the part of anti-Communist or anti-Jewish groups in the territories to be newly occupied must not be hampered. On the contrary, they are to be provoked although without leaving traces -- if necessary intensified and carefully guided in the right direction. This must be done in such a way that these local 'self-defense groups' will not be able to claim later on that they were given instructions or political assurances."*

Telex message of June 29, 1941, from the Chief of Security Police and Security Service, Reinhard Heydrich, to the commanders of the four "Einsatzgruppen" (Special Units)

▲ *"When I reached the square, around 15–20 bodies were lying there. They were cleared away by the Lithuanians, and the pools of blood were hosed away. ... Finally, another group of delinquents was driven and pushed into the square and, without any great fuss, simply beaten to death by civilians armed with iron bars..."*

Report by a sergeant of Baker's Company 562, 16th Army

Kovno (Kauen), June 1941

3.

▲ *"A young man ... with rolled up sleeves was armed with an iron crowbar. He yanked a man from a group [and] killed him with one or several blows to the back of his head. In this manner, within three quarters of an hour, he slew a group of from 45 to 50 persons."*

Report by a photographer on the pogrom at Kovno

■ *"... During the first hours after we had invaded, local anti-Semitic forces were prompted to start pogroms against the Jews, although this proved quite difficult.*

... From the outside it had to seem that the local population proper had taken these initial measures of their own accord in a natural reaction to decades of past oppression by the Jews and to Communist terror."

Report by F. W. Stahlecker, commander of Special Unit A

4. Pogrom in Lvov

■ *"FT: 4125 (encoded) Secret*

Provision of Illustrative Material

Continuing reports on the work of the Einsatzgruppen in the East should be provided to the Führer. For this purpose, especially interesting illustrative material, such as photos, posters, flyers and other documents are needed. If such material can be obtained or procured, I ask that it be sent as soon as possible."

Telex from Heinrich Müller, Chief of the Gestapo, to Special Units, August 1, 1941

Lvov (Lemberg), July 25–27, 1941

5. Shooting of Hostages

Schaulen, Lithuniua, 1941

■ *"I would like to state that as a result of the considerable emotional strain that accompanied such executions, numerous men proved after a while unable to carry out further shootings and thus had to be replaced. Conversely, there were other persons who could not get enough of it and who frequently volunteered for these executions."*

Testimony of Gustav Fix, former member of Special Unit 6

■ *"Buddies [of mine] sometimes refused to participate in executions. A few times I was also among these. And just as nothing was done to me by those in command, nothing was done to the others either after they had refused to carry out such orders. We were simply given different assignments. Thus we were not threatened with punitive measures, let alone facing a firing squad."*

A former lance corporal of the 322nd Police Battalion

These three people from Minsk, among them a Jewish girl, represent all those who were executed because they sided with the persecuted and against the persecutors.

■ *"In the city of Minsk, about 10,000 Jews were liquidated on July 28 and 29. Of these, 6,500 were Russian Jews -- overwhelmingly elderly, women, and children. The rest consisted of unemployable Jews, for the most part from Vienna, Brünn, Bremen, and Berlin, who by order of the Führer were sent to Minsk in November of last year."*

Report of July 31, 1942, by General Commissioner for White Russia (Belorussia) Wilhelm Kube

6. Execution of Partisans

Thousands were sent to the gallows or shot because they had hidden Jews, helped partisans, or personally fought against the occupying power.

Minsk, September 6, 1941

7. Before the Shooting

Odessa, October 22, 1941

■ *"Registration in Odessa. For official use only!*
649th Propaganda Company, Archive No. 23/27.
Photo: Sommerschuh, Text: Schöner.
Place: Odessa. Date: October 22, 1941.
Text: Criminal types at the proper place."

Notation at the back of the above photo

From October 23 to 25, 1941, 26,000 Jewish men from Odessa were shot by a Romanian special detachment in the course of a "retaliatory operation." The process resembled the massacre at Babi Yar, near Kiev, down to the last detail. That massacre had been committed a month earlier by Special Unit C.

8. The Route of the "Special Units"

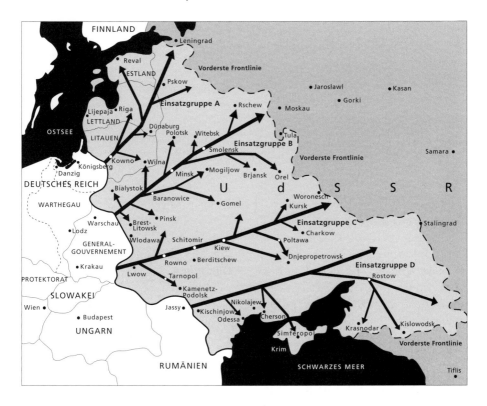

9. "Ghetto Clearance" in Kovno

■ "Following basic orders, the systematic purging operations in the eastern territories included, as far as possible, complete elimination of Jewry. Except for parts of the Ukraine, this objective has essentially been achieved with the execution of 229,052 Jews so far (see enclosure). Those remaining in the Baltic provinces are urgently needed for work and have been placed in ghettos... The isolation of the remaining Jews in special ghettos is also nearly com-

plete in the towns of the Ukraine. Requisite departments of the Army, the civilian administration, and German public authorities have committed them for labor duty to the utmost extent."

Secret activity report for the period October 16, 1941, to January 31, 1942, submitted by Special Unit A

10. Massacre at Lijepaja

Lijepaja (Libau), December 15, 1941

In Lijepaja, Latvia, 2,731 Jews and 23 Communists were shot between December 15 and 17, 1941 by German and Latvian police. The photos are from the office of the Libau branch of the Security Police. The photographer was the local Gestapo chief.

■ *"The executions of Jews carried out during the period under review are still talked about by the local populace. The lot of the Jews has aroused a good deal of pity, and few positive voices are heard in favor of the elimination of the Jews."*

Communication of January 3, 1942, by the local SS and police commander at Libau to the SS and police leader of Livonia

11. A Call-Up

Posters ordered the Jewish population of the town of Kislowodsk in the northern Caucasus to report to the freight yard at 5 a.m. on September 9, 1942. All who obeyed this order were transported by train to Mineralnije Vody and shot. After the German retreat, the first large mass grave with 6,000 dead bodies was found there. On August 5, 1943, Alexei Tolstoi published a report on this in Prawda.

12.

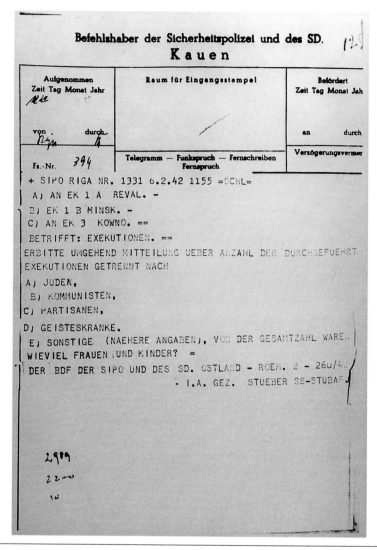

Befehlshaber der Sicherheitspolizei und des SD.

Kauen

Aufgenommen Zeit Tag Monat Jahr	Raum für Eingangsstempel	Befördert Zeit Tag Monat Jah
von . durch		an durch
Fs.-Nr. *394*	Telegramm — Funkspruch — Fernschreiben Fernspruch	Verzögerungsvermer

```
+ SIPO RIGA NR. 1331 6.2.42 1155 =SCHL=
A) AN EK 1 A REVAL. -
B) EK 1 B MINSK. -
C) AN EK 3 KOWNO. ==
BETRIFFT: EXEKUTIONEN. ==
ERBITTE UMGEHEND MITTEILUNG UEBER ANZAHL DER DURCHGEFUEHRT
EXEKUTIONEN GETRENNT NACH
A) JUDEN,
B) KOMMUNISTEN,
C) PARTISANEN,
D) GEISTESKRANKE.
E) SONSTIGE (NAEHERE ANGABEN), VON DER GESAMTZAHL WARE
WIEVIEL FRAUEN UND KINDER? =
DER BDF DER SIPO UND DES SD. OSTLAND - ROEM. 2 - 260/4..
                   - I.A. GEZ. STUEBER SS-STUBAF.
```

"... Regarding: Executions

Request immediate information on number of executions, broken down into:

A) Jews,
B) Communists,
C) Partisans,
D) mentally ill,
E) others (greater detail). Of the entire number, how many women and children?"

Signed, Stüber, SS Major

Inquiry by security police in Riga to special commandos in Reval, Minsk and Kovno

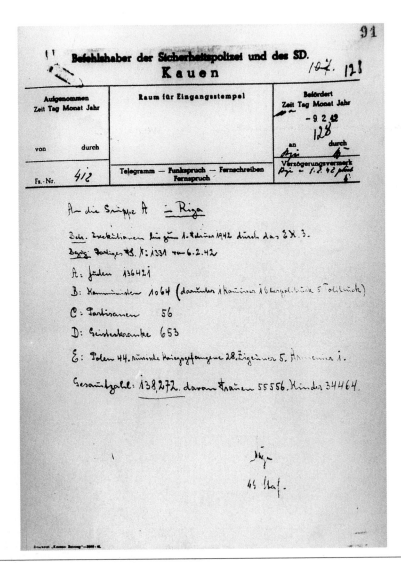

"... Regarding: Executions by EK [special commando] 3 until February 1, 1942.
Reference: your telex no. 1331 of 2/6/42

A) 136,421 Jews
B) 1,064 Communists (including 1 commissar, 1 senior political officer, 1 political officer)
C) 56 Partisans
D) 653 mentally ill
E) 44 Poles, 28 Russian prisoners of war, 5 Gypsies, 1 Armenian

Total – 138,272, including 55,556 women, 34,464 children."

Reply from special commando 3 in Kovno

13. Hitler's "Glorious Times"

In the Lodging of the "Ordnungspolizei"

Poster on photograph reads:
"It is glorious to live in a time that confronts people with great challenges." Adolf Hitler

■ *"We know that it is now futile to discuss various proposals for a solution; the Jewish Question has moved from a theoretical to a purely practical stage, not only in Germany, but to an increasing degree in other European countries as well... The fate of the Jews now proceeds according to the laws of an equity that does not succumb to petty emotions, but serves unerringly the welfare of all mankind. Judgment on the Jews of Europe has been passed!"*

The Front, Newspaper of an Army in the Field, No. 414, July 18, 1942

14. "A Page of Glory"

■ *"... 'The Jewish people are being exterminated,' every party member says. 'Of course, it's in our program, elimination of the Jews, extermination, we'll do it all right.' Among all those who talk like this, no one has witnessed it, no one has seen it through. Most of you will know, however, what it means to see 100 corpses lying together, or 500, or 1,000.*
To have stuck it out and at the same time to have remained decent -- aside from a few exceptions succumbing to human weakness -- that has made us tough. This is a page of glory in our history, unwritten and never to be written..."

Heinrich Himmler in Posen, October 4, 1943

Wlodawa, October 1942

Chronology

1941

May 2	*A conference of undersecretaries organised by Göring discusses the extermination of "umpteen people" in the Soviet Union through organised famines under German occupation*
May 23	*Economic policy guidelines for the occupation of the Soviet Union anticipate the deaths of "tens of millions"*
End of May	Activation of four "Special Units" in Pretzsch (Saxony) to prepare for killing operations in the Soviet Union
June 6	*"Commissar Order" provides for shooting all captured political commissars in the impending war*
June 21	*Himmler orders the drafting of "General Plan for the East," which projects the "evacuation" of more than 30 million people. The "Ministry for the East" upgrades this figure to 50 million*
June 22	*German invasion of the Soviet Union*
June 23	The "special units" and individual commandos begin to organize pogroms and mass executions
June 23–28	Pogrom in Kovno
June 25	Pogrom in Jassy (15,000 dead)
July 1 to August 31	Massacre by "Special Unit" D, the Army, and special Romanian units throughout Bessarabia (150,000 dead)
July	Special Commando 9 in Vilnius (5,000 dead)
July 4–11	Pogrom in Tarnopol (5,000 dead)
July 13 to August 9	Massacre in Dvinsk (9,000 dead)
July 20	Ghetto set up in Minsk
July 24	Massacre in Kishinev ends (10,000 dead); establishment of a ghetto
July 25–27	Pogrom in Lvov ("Operation Petljura")
August 5–7	Massacre in Pinsk (11,000 dead)
August 19	Massacre in Mogilev (3,700 dead)
August 27–28	Massacre in Kamenetz-Podolsk (23,600 dead)
August 31 to Sept. 3	Massacre in Ponary, near Vilnius (8,000 dead)
September 1	*Because of protests from the clergy, the "euthanasia" operation in Germany is temporarily halted (70,000 – 93,000 dead)*
September 15	Massacre near Berdichev (18,600 dead)
September 15 to October 13	Deportation of 150,000 Jews from Bessarabia and the Bukovina region to Transnistria, where 90,000 of them perish
September 19	Massacre in Zhitomir ends (10,000 dead)
Sept. 29–30	Mass shootings of Jews from Kiev by Special Commando 4a in the ravine of Babi Yar (33,771 dead)
October to December	"Operations" in Vilnius (33,500 dead)
October 8	Liquidation of the Vitebsk Ghetto (16,000 dead)
October 13	Massacre in Dnepropetrovsk (20,000 dead)
October 15	Deportations from Germany and Austria to Lodz, Kovno, Minsk, and Riga
Oct. 23–25	Massacre in Odessa (19,000 dead)
October 28	"Operation" in Fort IX near Kovno (9,000 dead). 17,412 people remain in the ghetto
November 7	Massacre in Minsk (12,000 dead)
November 7–8	Massacre in Rovno (21,000 dead)
November 7–9	Additional massacre in Dvinsk (3,000 dead)
November 20	Additional massacre in Minsk (20,000 dead)
November 20 to December 7	Mass shootings in the forests around Riga (30,000 dead)
December 6	*Soviet Russian counteroffensive outside Moscow begins*
Dec. 21–31	Mass shootings in Camp Bogdanovka (46,000 dead)

(Incomplete overview of the first half year of German occupation)

6. The Wannsee Conference

In July 1941, Heydrich had Göring assign him to prepare the "Final Solution of the Jewish Question in Europe," which was intended to involve over 11 million people. This was only the first stage of a much more far-reaching, comprehensive undertaking. "European reconstruction along racial-political lines," for which Himmler developed his "General Plan for the East," projected the compulsory "resettlement" of 30 million Slavs; experts estimated 50 million.

When the Wannsee Conference was held on January 20,1942, mass executions had been going on in the Soviet Union for half a year, deportations from Germany had begun, and Chelmno, the first extermination camp, had already been operative for six weeks.

It was the first joint gathering of top ranking representatives of the ministerial bureaucracy and the SS. As chief of the security police and security service, Heydrich wanted to inform those present about the assignment received from the Reich Security Main Office, have its leading role affirmed, and secure the cooperation of all ministerial departments, without which his plans could not have been realized. The participants at the conference were not to offer any resolutions of their own, but merely to confer about the implementation of a decision that originated with Hitler.

All but two of the state secretaries present were in fact well informed about the regional deportations and killing operations already in progress. The representatives of the SS were directly involved in them. And anyone not yet aware of all the details was informed in the course of the conference. Heydrich had expected that his concept would meet with misgivings and objections from the ministerial departments, but he encountered only general agreement and readiness to help in its execution.

The discussions dealt solely with details. The representative of the Ministry for Foreign Affairs suggested beginning deportations in those countries where they could be carried out without major difficulties. The secretary of the Interior Ministry recommended that "Mischlinge" (offspring of mixed marriages) not be deported, but undergo compulsory sterilisation instead. The secretary of the Commissioner for the Four-Year-Plan demanded a temporary exemption of skilled Jewish workers in plants essential to the war effort, and the deputy to the Governor General in Cracow pleaded urgently to have the "Final Solution" start with the Jews in Poland.

As Eichmann was subsequently to affirm in his Jerusalem trial of 1961, the various technical aspects of mass murder were quite openly discussed. But even the consciously veiled wording of the protocol, which was, in fact, rewritten several times, betrays the horrible truth to the careful reader.

The Madagascar Project

Paris, July 1940

From the summer of 1940, Hitler dominated western Europe. His troops paraded down the Champs Elysées. Millions of Jews were at the mercy of the Germans. For a brief period of time, the Reich Security Main Office and the Foreign Office discussed the old project of establishing a "Jewish reservation" on Madagascar, with France handing over the island to Germany as part of a peace treaty. As soon as England had been vanquished and the sea lanes opened, Madagascar was to be transformed into a mammoth ghetto, guarded by the SS, for the Jews of Europe. However, in summer 1941 the decision was made to invade the Soviet Union and carry out the "Final Solution" in Eastern Europe. The Madagascar Project was shelved.

Biographies of the Participants

Reinhard Heydrich (1904–1942) Chief of Security Police and Security Service

Born in Halle, the son of a composer and director of a conservatory. Catholic high school. Freecorps fighter in 1920. Joined the German Navy in 1922. In 1926, appointed naval lieutenant, intelligence and signal officer. Dishonorable discharge as first lieutenant in 1931. Joined the Nazi Party and the SS in 1931. In July 1932, Himmler entrusted Heydrich with organisation of the Security Service (SD) for the surveillance of political opponents.

Became head of the Bavarian Political Police in 1933 and head of the Secret State Police Office in Berlin in 1934. Named head of the Main Office of the Security Service in January 1935, Chief of Security Police in June 1936, and Head of the Reich Security Main Office in October 1939. Fighter pilot in April-May 1940. In June 1941, ordered the "Special Units" to carry out pogroms and executions in the Soviet Union. At the end of July 1941, he received authorization from Göring to lay the groundwork for a "General Solution of the Jewish Question," which he had earlier requested. In September 1941, Heydrich became Deputy Reich Protector of Bohemia and Moravia.

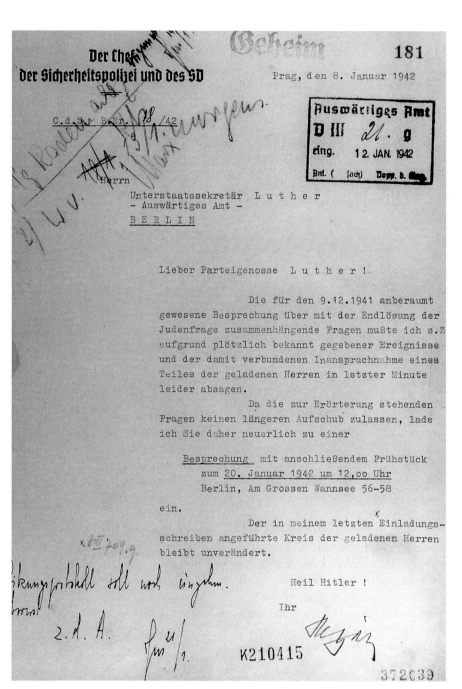

Der Chef
der Sicherheitspolizei und des SD

Geheim

Prag, den 8. Januar 1942

C.d.S. B.Nr. 18/42

Auswärtiges Amt
D III 21. g
eing. 1 2. JAN. 1942
Pol. (fach) Depp. b.

Herrn

Unterstaatssekretär L u t h e r
- Auswärtiges Amt -
B E R L I N

Lieber Parteigenosse L u t h e r !

Die für den 9.12.1941 anberaumt
gewesene Besprechung über mit der Endlösung der
Judenfrage zusammenhängende Fragen mußte ich s.Z
aufgrund plötzlich bekannt gegebener Ereignisse
und der damit verbundenen Inanspruchnahme eines
Teiles der geladenen Herren in letzter Minute
leider absagen.

Da die zur Erörterung stehenden
Fragen keinen längeren Aufschub zulassen, lade
ich Sie daher neuerlich zu einer

Besprechung mit anschließendem Frühstück
zum 20. Januar 1942 um 12,oo Uhr
Berlin, Am Grossen Wannsee 56-58

ein.

Der in meinem letzten Einladungs-
schreiben angeführte Kreis der geladenen Herren
bleibt unverändert.

Heil Hitler !

Ihr

z.d.A.

K210415

372039

Invitation of Senior Legation Councillor Luther to the Wannsee Conference

At the Wannsee Conference, Heydrich submitted a report on a general plan for the genocide of over eleven million Jews, to be deported "to the East." At the same time he asked for "cooperation" from the various ministries represented at the conference. On May 27, 1942, Czech resistance fighters made an attempt on his life in Prague. He died of his wounds on June 4, 1942.

Dr. Rudolf Lange
(1910–1945)
Security Police
and
Security Service

Born in Weisswasser (district of Liegnitz), son of a railway construction supervisor. Studied law, and in 1933 worked for the Gestapo in Halle. Joined the stormtroopers in November 1933. Doctor of law degree in 1934. Employed by the Secret State Police Office in 1936, he joined the Nazi Party and the SS in 1937. Worked for the Vienna Gestapo in 1938. In 1939, Lange became an administrative councilor with the Gestapo in Stuttgart. SS captain and chief of the Weimar and Erfurt Gestapo in 1940. In September 1940, he was named deputy to the chief of the Berlin Gestapo. Attained rank of SS major in 1941. Lange went to Riga in June 1941 with "Special Unit A" and became chief of the Riga Gestapo and Criminal Police in July 1941. In charge of "Special Commando 2," which by December 1941 had killed roughly 60,000 Jews from Latvia, as well as Jews from Germany and Austria who had been deported to Riga. In December 1941, he was named commander of the Security Police and Security Service in Latvia.

Lange participated in the Wannsee Conference on January 20, 1942 as representative of the Senior SS and Police Leader for northern Russia and Ostland, SS Lieutenant General Friedrich Jeckeln. Lange carried out further killing operations against Jews, political opponents, and partisans in Latvia, using gas vans from 1942 on. He became a senior administrative councilor and SS lieutenant colonel in 1943. In October 1944, he became acting commander of the Security Police and Security Service in the Warta region. In January 1945, Lange was promoted to SS colonel. He was killed in Poznan in February 1945 while trying to recapture his headquarters.

Dr. Eberhard Schöngarth
(1903–1946)
Security Police
and
Security Service

Born in Leipzig, son of a construction supervisor. High school; participant in the Kapp Putsch of 1920. Joined the Nazi Party and the stormtroopers in 1922, worked as a bank employee. Doctor of law degree in June 1929; assistant judge in June 1932. Joined the SS in 1933. In November 1933 he went to work for the Reich Post Office at Erfurt, in 1935 joined the Press Section of the Secret State Police Office, and then became head of the section in charge of church affairs. Schöngarth became an administrative councilor in 1936, then head of the Gestapo in Dortmund, Bielefeld, and Münster, later of the Gestapo in Erfurt.

In 1939, he became senior administrative councilor and SS lieutenant colonel. In January 1941, he was named commander of the Security Police and Security Service in the Generalgouvernement, based in Cracow. Became a police colonel in February 1941. During July and August 1941 he led a special unit in Lvov.

Schöngarth participated in the Wannsee Conference on January 20, 1942; ten days later, he was promoted to SS brigadier general and brigadier general of police. In 1943 he joined the Waffen SS in Greece, and in June 1944 became commander of the Security Police and Security Service in the occupied Netherlands. In March 1945, following an assassination attempt on the local SS and police leader, SS lieutenant general Hanns Rauter, he had 250 hostages shot before taking over Rauter's duties.

In February 1946, Schöngarth was sentenced to death by a British military court in Westerland and executed.

Adolf Eichmann
(1906–1962)
Reich Security
Main Office

Born in Solingen, son of a bookkeeper. After abandoning his studies, he worked as a salesman from 1925 to 1927, then as a sales representative. Joined the Nazi Party and the SS in April 1932. Military training in 1933; active in the fall of 1934 in the SS Security Service (SD) in Berlin, and as of 1935 in Section II/112 (Jewry). Director of the Centers for Jewish Emigration in Vienna and Prague in 1938–1939. Drew up plans for a "Jewish reservation" in Nisko on the river San (Poland) in October 1939. In December 1939, Eichmann took over Section IV D4 (Emigration, Evacuation) in the Reich Security Main Office, then Section IV B4 (Jewish Affairs and Evacuations) in March 1941. In August 1941, he visited Auschwitz and discussed plans for deportation and extermination. Eichmann was made an SS lieutenant colonel in November 1941.

Inspection of Theresienstadt Ghetto on January 19, 1942; the following day, he participated in and served as secretary to the Wannsee Confer-

From the Protocol of the Wannsee Conference

"... In lieu of emigration, evacuation of the Jews to the east has emerged as an additional possible solution, now that the Führer's prior authorization has been obtained.

But although these operations are to be regarded solely as temporary measures, practical experience has already been gathered here and will be of major importance for the upcoming solution of the Jewish question.

In the course of this final solution to the question of European Jewry, some 11 million Jews come under consideration ...

The Jews are to be sent in a suitable manner and under appropriate supervision to labor in the east. Separated by sex, Jews able to work will be led in large labor columns into these areas while building roads. In the process, many will undoubtedly fall away through natural attrition.

The remainder that conceivably will still be around and undoubtedly constitutes the sturdiest segment will have to be dealt with accordingly, as it represents a natural selection which, if left at liberty, must be considered a nucleus of new Jewish development (see the lesson of history).

In the course of the practical implementation of the final solution, Europe will be combed through from west to east. Priority will have to be given to the area of the Reich, including the Protectorate of Bohemia and Moravia, if only because of housing shortages and other sociopolitical needs.

The evacuated Jews will initially be brought without delay to so-called transit ghettos, and transported from there further to the east ...

The starting point of the major evacuation will depend largely on military developments. With regard to the treatment of the final solution in those European regions occupied or influenced by us, it was suggested that appropriate specialists at the Foreign Office join with whoever is the official handling this matter for the Security Police and Security Service ..."

ence. Between 1942 and 1944, Eichmann coordinated the deportations and mass murder of millions. Sent to Budapest in March 1944 as head of "Special Detachment Eichmann" to prepare the deportation of over 437,000 Jews.

In early May 1945 he posed as an air force private; he was captured, but escaped. Worked under false name as a forestry worker near Celle; fled to Italy in 1950 and on to Argentina. Kidnapped by members of the Israeli Intelligence Service in May 1960. Sentenced to death in Jerusalem in December 1961. Executed on May 31, 1962.

Heinrich Müller
(1900–?)
Reich Security
Main Office

Born in Munich, son of a policeman. Elementary school, then training as an airplane mechanic. Volunteered for war service in 1917 and received flight training. Served on the western front in 1918; demobilized as a corporal in 1919. Thereafter, employee in Munich Police Headquarters. Secretary with the Munich Political Police in 1929, operating against Communist organizations.

In 1933, advanced to senior police secretary and detective inspector within the Police Criminal Investigation Division. Joined the SS in April 1934, transferred to the Secret State Police Office in Berlin. Deputy chief of the Political Police Section in the Main Office of Security Police in 1936. Became an SS colonel, senior executive officer, and chief criminal investigator in 1937. Applied for membership in the Nazi Party. In 1939, became manager of the Reich Central Office for Jewish Emigration and SS Oberführer. Starting in early September 1939, issued instructions for "special treatment" (murder) of political prisoners. Head of Department IV (Gestapo) of the Reich Security Main Office in October 1939. Became SS brigadier general and brigadier general of police in December 1940; SS major general and major general of police in November 1941.

Participant in the Wannsee Conference on January 20, 1942. Issued an order in November 1942 to deport all Jews and persons of "mixed blood" from German concentration camps to Auschwitz. In 1945, Müller probably escaped from Berlin to Rome and then South America.

Otto Hofmann
(1896–1982)
SS Race and
Settlement
Main Office

Born in Innsbruck, son of a businessman. Volunteered for military service in August 1914, made second lieutenant in March 1917. Taken prisoner of war in Russia in June 1917, escaped in August, then trained as a pilot. Demobilized in 1919. Worked in the wholesale wine business from 1920–1925, and later as a self-employed wine salesman. Joined the Nazi Party in 1923 and the SS in April 1931. Starting in 1933, Hofmann was a full-time SS leader.

In 1934, commander of the 21st SS Regiment (Magdeburg) and, in 1935, of SS Sector XV (Hamburg). Director of the Genealogical Section within the SS Race and Settlement Main Office in 1939; head of that office in 1940, he became responsible for German settlements in occupied Poland, the "Germanization" of Polish children, and SS "genealogical preservation" *(Sippenpflege).* Became an SS major general in 1941.

As a participant in the Wannsee Conference, Hofmann called primarily for sterilization of persons of "mixed blood." In April 1943, he was named commander of the SS Main Sector Southwest and senior SS and police leader in Württemberg, Baden, and the Alsace. In June of the same year, he advanced to SS lieutenant general and police lieutenant general, and in July 1944 to lieutenant general of the Waffen SS as well. He was also commandant of prisoners of war within Defense Sector V (Southeast).

In the trial of the Main Office for Race and Settlement in March 1948, he was sentenced to 25 years imprisonment for crimes against humanity and war crimes. Amnestied in 1954 and released from Landsberg penitentiary. Worked thereafter as a business clerk in Württemberg. Died in late 1982.

Wilhelm Kritzinger (1890–1947) Reich Chancellery

Born a parson's son in Grünfier (Netze district). Studied law; served from 1914–1918 at the front, ultimately as a second lieutenant. Prisoner of war in France from 1918–1920. Assessor in 1921, then employed in the Reich Ministry of Justice. Associate judge with the Prussian Ministry of Trade in 1925–1926. Returned to Reich Ministry of Justice in 1926. Became ministerial junior assistant secretary in 1930. Participated in 1934 in drafting a law to legalize the killings of June 30, 1934. Several jurisdictional conflicts with the Gestapo in 1935–1936 regarding "protective custody." For this reason, Kritzinger applied in 1938 for a transfer to the Reich Chancellery, where he served as section leader with the rank of ministerial secretary. Joined the Nazi Party.

In 1939 and 1940, participated in drafting decrees against "parasites"

[Volksschädlinge] and the 11th supplementary ordinance to the Reich Citizenship Law, which provided the legal justification for confiscating the property of German Jews prior to their deportation.

Kritzinger took part in the Wannsee Conference on January 20, 1942, and was soon after appointed assistant undersecretary. In November 1942 he became an undersecretary in the Reich Chancellery, responsible for all five sections. In 1942 and 1943, he participated in depriving the Jews of further rights.

Fled Berlin in April 1945, and became undersecretary in the Dönitz Government at Flensburg in May. Then interned in Bruchsal. Released in April 1946; arrested again in December of that year. During questioning before the International Military Tribunal at Nuremberg in 1947, Kritzinger declared himself ashamed of the Nazi crimes. Released from detention shortly before his death in October 1947.

Dr. Gerhard Klopfer (1905–1987) Nazi Party Chancellery

Born in Schreibersdorf near Lauban (Silesia), son of a farmer. Freecorps volunteer in 1923. Doctor of law degree in 1927; appointed judge to a Düsseldorf district court in 1931. Joined the Nazi Party and the Stormtroopers in April 1933. At the end of 1933, became a departmental official in the Prussian Ministry of Agriculture, 1934 in the Secret State Police Office. Moved from there in April 1935 to the Staff of the "Führer's Deputy," Rudolf Hess. Joined the SS in 1935 and became section manager on Hess's staff. Senior executive officer in 1936. As a ministerial junior assistant secretary in 1938, he dealt with the expropriation of Jewish businesses.

In 1939, Klopfer became an SS colonel and ministerial assistant secretary. Made ministerial secretary and director of the division for State law matters of the newly established Nazi Party Chancellery under Martin Bormann in 1941. Responsible, among other things, for questions of race and national characteristics, economic policies, cooperation with the Reich Security Main Office, and principals of occupation policies.

Klopfer participated in the Wannsee Conference on January 20, 1942. In 1943, as an undersecretary in the Party Chancellery, he helped further restrict the rights of those living in "mixed marriages". Became an SS major general in 1944.

Fled Berlin in April 1945, later interned. After his release from detention in 1949, the superior Denazification Court at Nuremberg pronounced him "1ess incriminated." He became a tax advisor in 1952, and a lawyer in Ulm in 1956. In 1962, the state prosecutor's office of that city stayed all further legal proceedings concerning his participation in the Wannsee Conference. Died in Ulm in February 1987.

Martin Luther
(1895–1945)
German Foreign
Office

Born in Berlin, son of a privy councilor. High school diploma, war service 1914–1917. From 1917–1919 assigned to the Prussian Ministry of War and promoted to the rank of lieutenant. Subsequently worked as a shipping agent.

Joined the Nazi Party in March 1932. In 1933–1934, served as head of the Economic Consulting Center in Berlin-Zehlendorf, where he became an honorary city councillor in 1936. Also headed the Party Consulting Center at the Office of the Representative of the Nazi Party for Foreign Political Affairs, Joachim von Ribbentrop. After the latter was appointed foreign minister, Luther was appointed legation councillor first class in charge of the "Special Section on the Nazi Party" within the Foreign Office in December 1938. He was named senior legation councillor and director of "Department Ger-

many" in 1939. Liaison between the Foreign Office and the SS, in particular to the "Section for Jewish Affairs" of the Reich Security Main Office. Became envoy first class in 1940. In December 1941, he drafted a memorandum to Ribbentrop on the killing activities of the "Special Units" in the Soviet Union.

On January 20, 1942, Luther participated in the Wannsee Conference as an assistant undersecretary. He recommended that the Nordic countries be omitted initially on account of the small number of Jews and of possible complications that might arise, and advised concentrating on southeastern and western Europe instead.

Thereafter, Eichmann and Luther cooperated closely. In February 1943, Luther was sent to Sachsenhausen Concentration Camp after a joint attempt with the SS to topple Ribbentrop. He was released in April 1945 and died a month later in Berlin.

Dr. Josef Bühler
(1904–1948)
Office of the
Governor
General
at Cracow

Born in Waldsee (Württemberg), son of a baker. Doctorate in Law in 1932. Joined the Nazi Party in April 1933.

As a senior public prosecutor, he was office manager for Hans Frank, Reich minister without portfolio. Promoted in 1939 to ministerial junior assistant secretary; in December of that year, became office head for Governor General Hans Frank at Cracow. In March 1940 he became Frank's undersecretary, and in July 1941 his deputy. Participated in the introduction of distinguishing marks for Jews, the establishment of ghettos, and the "special pacification operation" of May-June 1940, in which 3,500 Polish intellectuals were killed.

On the morning of January 20, 1942, Bühler and Heydrich had a private talk. Bühler urged at the Wannsee Conference that "the final solution of this question should begin in the *Generalgouvernement,* where transportation problems play only a minor role, and questions pertaining to deployment of labor would not impede the course of this operation."

Involved in planning for the establishment of German settlements at Lublin and Zamosc, and in the deportation of Poles to Germany for forced labor.

Fled Cracow in January 1945. In April 1946, witness for Frank at the International Military Tribunal at Nuremberg. Thereafter extradited to Poland. Sentenced to death in Cracow in July, executed in August 1948.

Dr. Roland
Freisler
(1893–1945)
Reich Ministry
of Justice

Born in Celle, son of an engineer. War service as officer cadet in 1914, prisoner of war in Russia in October 1915. Close contacts with the Bolsheviks. Return to Germany in 1920. Doctor of law degree in 1922 from Jena University. From 1924 on, worked as a lawyer in Kassel and as city councilor for the Völkisch-Social bloc. Joined the Nazi Party in July 1925 and worked regularly for the party on political crime cases.

In March 1933, participated in the assault on Kassel's city hall and courthouse. Appointed ministerial secretary at the Prussian Ministry of Justice; became undersecretary in June 1933. In June 1934, Freisler was named undersecretary in the newly-combined Reich and Prussian Ministry of Justice, in charge, among other things, of personnel, penal legislation, and execution of sentences. In 1939, Freisler called for stricter laws and greater authority for special courts, "courts-martial on the domestic front." He participated in the Wannsee Conference as representative of Undersecretary Franz Schlegelberger, acting minister in the Reich Ministry of Justice.

As President of the "People's Court" *(Volksgerichtshof)* starting in August 1942, Freisler presided over 1,200 trials of political adversaries. Nearly all ended with the death penalty. Died during an air raid in the courtyard of the "People's Court" in Berlin on February 3, 1945.

Erich Neumann (1892–1948) Office of the Plenipotentiary for the Four Year Plan

Born in Forst (Lower Lusatia), son of a factory owner, studied law. War service 1914–1917, ultimately as first lieutenant. Legal internship 1917–1920, government assessor in the Prussian Ministry of the Interior in 1920, then at the Essen District Office. Senior executive officer in the Prussian Ministry of Commerce in 1923. District president *(Landrat)* in Freystadt (Lower Silesia) 1926–1928. Then returned to the Prussian Ministry of Commerce as ministerial junior assistant secretary. Head of department in the Prussian Ministry of State and in charge of administrative reforms as of September 1932. Joined the Nazi Party in May 1933, and the SS with the rank of major in August 1934. Entered the Prussian Ministry of State at the end of 1935, becoming head of the Working Team for the Observation of the Domestic and Foreign Economic Situation. In October 1936, became director of Section 6 (foreign currency) in the Office of the Plenipotentiary for the Four Year Plan, headed by Hermann Göring. In summer 1938 he was named undersecretary; in November, he participated in a meeting of Göring's on the "Aryanization of the Economy" and distinguishing markings for, and isolation of, the Jews. In 1941, Neumann became deputy chairman of the board of trustees of the Continental Petroleum Corporation, entrusted with the exploitation of oil resources in the occupied territories of the Soviet Union.

At the Wannsee Conference on January 20, 1942, Neumann represented the Ministries of Economy, Labor, Finances, Food, Transportation, and Armaments and Munition. He requested that Jewish workers in firms essential to the war effort not be deported for the time being. From August 1942 until May 1945, he was general manager of the German Potassium Syndicate. After the war he was interned, but was released for health reasons early in 1948. Died soon after.

Dr. Wilhelm Stuckart (1902–1953) Reich Ministry of the Interior

Born in Wiesbaden, son of a railroad employee. Membership in nationalist youth groups. Joined the Nazi Party in 1922 and participated in the Hitler Putsch in 1923. Doctor of Law in 1928, judge in a lower district court in 1930. Lawyer in Stettin in 1932. Became undersecretary in the Prussian Ministry of Sciences in 1933, in the Reich Ministry of Sciences in 1934, and in the Reich Ministry of the Interior in 1935. Co-author of the Nuremberg Racial Laws. In 1940, involved in preparations to deprive Jews of their citizenship. In August 1941, he took part in a conference on the "Germanization" of parts of the Soviet Union.

As a participant in the Wannsee Conference on January 20, 1942, Stuckart proposed compulsory sterilization of persons of "mixed blood" [Mischlinge] as well as compulsory divorces of "mixed marriages." Ten days later, he was appointed SS major general. In April 1943, he chaired a conference of undersecretaries on "police retaliation against criminal acts committed by Jews." He advanced to SS lieutenant general in 1944.

Interned in May 1945, as minister of the interior in the Dönitz Government at Flensburg. Denied in 1947 that he had participated in the Wannsee Conference. In April 1949, he received a prison sentence of three years and ten months which, because of his preceding detention, was counted as having been served. Thereafter as city treasurer in Helmstedt, then manager of the Institute

for the Promotion of the Economy in Lower Saxony. In October 1951, became third regional chairman of the "League of Expellees and Disenfranchised." A denazification court classified him in 1953 as a "fellow traveller" and fined him 500 Marks. Died November 15, 1953 in a traffic accident.

Dr. Georg Leibbrandt (1899–1982) Reich Ministry for the Occupied Eastern Territories

Born in Hoffnungsfeld near Odessa, son of a farmer. High school in Dorpat and Odessa, Freecorps fighter in 1919, flight to Berlin. Study of theology, philosophy, history, and political economy starting in 1920. Ph.D. in 1927, thereafter three study trips to the Soviet Union. Employed in the Reich Central Archive in 1929.

Student in the USA 1931–1933; there propagandist for the Nazi Party. Leibbrandt applied for membership in the party in 1933 and became director of "Section East" in the Nazi Foreign Policy Department. Thereafter in charge of anti-Communist and anti-Soviet Russian propaganda in the "Rosenberg Bureau."

Became associate judge of the "People's Court" (Volksgerichtshof) in 1938, and director of the Main Political Department in the Reich Ministry for the Occupied Eastern Territories in July 1941. In October 1941, Leibbrandt participated in a meeting with Heydrich on ways to include all Jews in the extermination program. Participant in the Wannsee Conference on January 20, 1942. Two days later Leibbrandt called a meeting on how to define the term "Jew" in the "Eastern Territories." In February 1943, he drew up a memorandum regarding a Russian national committee and an anti-Soviet Russian "Liberation army". In summer 1943, he reported for duty in the navy.

Leibbrandt was interned in 1945; following release from detention in 1949, he became active in an American cultural institute in Munich. A preliminary investigation by the district court of Nuremberg-Fürth, begun in January 1950, was dropped in August 1950. No further attempts were made to prosecute him. He died in 1982.

Dr. Alfred Meyer
(1891–1945)
Reich Ministry
for the Occupied
Eastern
Territories

Born in Göttingen, son of a governmental councilor and building official. High school diploma, then officer cadet in 1912, company commander in 1914, subsequently battalion commander. Prisoner of war in France in 1917, discharged as a captain in 1920. Commercial employee, student of political economy. Ph. D. in political science in 1922; legal adviser to a Gelsenkirchen mining firm from 1923 to 1930. Joined the Nazi Party in 1928; local branch leader; party district leader of Emscher-Lippe, 1929–1930. Became Reichstag delegate in September 1930 and Nazi Party provincial leader (Gauleiter) of Northern Westphalia in 1931. Appointed deputy governor (Reichsstatthalter) of Lippe and Schaumburg-Lippe in May 1933 and head of the state government of Lippe in 1936. Meyer became governor of the province of Westphalia and lieutenant general in the Stormtroopers (SA) in 1938.

Meyer took over leadership of the civilian administration of an army in 1939, and was acting Reich Defense Commissioner of Defense District VI (northern Westphalia). In 1941 he was appointed an undersecretary and deputy to Minister Alfred Rosenberg in the Reich Ministry for the Occupied Eastern Territories, responsible for three main departments: politics, administration, and economy.

At the Wannsee Conference on January 20, 1942, Meyer urged that "certain preparatory work" be carried out "on the spot at the places in question, yet without creating unrest among the civilian population". In July 1942, he suggested subjecting persons of "mixed blood" in the Soviet Union to the same "measures" applied to Jews.

In 1942, Meyer was substantially involved in mass deportations of Soviet forced laborers. He was Reich Defense Commissioner of Northern Westphalia starting in November 1942. Found dead in the spring of 1945; presumably suicide.

Topography of Power
(Map of Berlin, see room 6)

"Europe will be combed through from west to east"
(Map of occupied Europe, see room 6)

From Planning to Action

Only a few days after the Wannsee Conference, Adolf Eichmann informed all administrative offices of the Gestapo that the "final solution of the Jewish question" had been set in motion. He ordered lists to be drawn up within one week of all Jews still living in Germany. Simultaneously, he announced which groups of persons were to be temporarily exempted from deportation. The criteria for this had been determined at the Wannsee Conference.

In May 1942, Chief of the Gestapo Heinrich Müller let it be known that all Jews in Germany had been registered for "evacuation" With that, the groundwork was laid for all subsequent deportations. Nearly all of those whom the Gestapo "evacuated" during the following months to the Lublin district and to Minsk were killed almost immediately upon their arrival.

Chronology

1939

September 21 — Heydrich holds meeting with commanders of "special units" on "the Jewish question in the occupied territories," the "final objective" and steps leading.

1940

January 30 — Heydrich, Seyss-Inquart and leading Gestapo officials from Poland meet on "resettlement projects"

1941

June 17 — Heydrich holds meeting with the commanders of the four "special units" on their mission

June 22 — *German attack on the Soviet Union*

July 31 — Göring assigns Heydrich to prepare the ground for the "final solution of the Jewish question"

October 10 — Heydrich holds meeting with Eichmann and SS leaders on the "Solution of the Jewish Question" in the Protectorate of Bohemia and Moravia and the "Altreich" [Germany within its 1937 borders]

1942

January 20 — Wannsee Conference

January 29 — Departmental meeting within the Reich Ministry for the Occupied Territories on how exactly to define the term "Jew"

February 23 — Departmental meeting within the Foreign Office on how to treat the "enemy property" of deported Jews

March 6 — Meeting of Section IV B 4 of the Reich Security Main Office on sterilization of "persons of mixed blood" and divorce of "mixed marriages"
Meeting of Section IV 4 B of the Reich Security Main Office with all "experts on Jews" on the projected deportations

June 11 — Meeting of Section IV B 4 of the Reich Security Main Office with "specialists on Jews" from Paris, The Hague, and Brussels on the projected deportations from France, The Netherlands, and Belgium

July 30 — Departmental meeting within the Foreign Office on "treatment of Jewish property abroad and of property of foreign Jews within the Reich"

August 28 — Meeting of Section IV B 4 of the Reich Security Main Office with "specialists on Jews" to discuss the overall progress of the deportations

September 25 — Departmental meeting on "restriction of Jewish rights" and forfeiture of their property to the state

Sept. 26–28 — Meeting on deportations from the Generalgouvernement and Romania

October 27 — Further meeting of Section IV B 4 of the Reich Security Main Office to discuss sterilization of "persons of mixed blood" and divorce of "mixed marriages"

1943

April 21 — Departmental meeting within the Reich Ministry of the Interior on "restriction of Jewish rights" and forfeiture of their property following divorce of Jews living in "mixed marriage"

This is an incomplete reconstruction. Regular meetings took place between the Reich Security Main Office (RSHA) and participating agencies in Berlin and elsewhere on deportations (only a few of which are listed here), as well as meetings between the RSHA and the Reich Ministry of Transportation about timetables, and discussions with the Foreign Office.

7. Deportations

In all European countries occupied by the German armed forces, and in the countries allied with Germany, the same tragedy repeated itself. It always began with Jews being listed and registered, marked and deprived of their rights, and ended with their transport to extermination camps. The deportations began in Germany and Poland at the end of 1941, were extended in the early summer to western Europe, and culminated two years later with the deportation and murder of the Hungarian Jews.

Everything was governed by regulations and went according to a precise plan. Each household received written instructions as to what and how much a person was permitted to take along: one backpack with provisions, mess kit and spoon, no knives or scissors, two blankets, sheets, warm clothing and heavy shoes -- maximum total weight 25 kilograms. Valuables had to be turned in, additional property registered, house keys surrendered. A truck was already waiting on the street to drive the Jews to an assembly camp or directly to the railway station. At the loading ramp stood a train with 20 freight cars, their ventilation windows nailed shut with barbed wire, and two passenger cars for the guard detail. Each transport held 1000 persons. The trains left several times a week from railway stations all over Europe: from Berlin and Warsaw, Amsterdam and Paris, Prague and Budapest, Oslo and Athens. The frequently lasted several days and nights. Worn out from lack of sleep, dirty, thirsty, and desperate, the deportees were carried toward unknown destinations whose names are today familiar to the entire world.

Initially, people complied with the order to report with their baggage for "resettlement." To deceive them, they were told they would be sent to Poland to work. After the first rumors leaked from the camps, many younger people tried to go into hiding. The suicide rate increased among the sick and elderly. Any who did not report voluntarily to the collecting point were fetched by the police. To fill the trains, entire city districts were combed through during roundups.

These manhunts were organized by the Reich Security Main Office. The Reich Transportation Ministry, with the German Reichsbahn under its jurisdiction, furnished the trains and arranged the schedules. Willing helpers were found nearly everywhere, in Germany as well as in the occupied countries.

Wherever diplomatic considerations remained essential and appearances had to be preserved, the Foreign Ministry handled negotiations. Some countries that had initially adopted German-style anti-Semitic legislation subsequently either refused to yield to German pressure, or did so only hesitantly. Often they merely handed over foreign and stateless Jews who had entered the country as they fled from the German armies. But for the great majority of Jews in occupied Europe, there was no escape.

1. The Guidelines

■ *"III. Transport. It is recommended that the Jews to be evacuated be concentrated before deportation. Transports will take place containing 1,000 Jews each (larger numbers are impermissible) according to a timetable issued in cooperation with the Reich Ministry of Transportation, which will be passed on to the office involved.*

Each person must take along:

Legal tender of 50 RM in Reich Credit Institute Notes or 100 Zloty. A suitcase or knapsack with equipment (no locked goods)
Complete clothing (sturdy footwear)
Bedclothes and blanket
Food for 2 weeks (bread, flour, barley, beans)
Eating utensils (plate or pot) with spoon."

"Guidelines for Technical Implementation of Evacuation of Jews to the East (Auschwitz concentration camp)." Circular by Reich Main Security Office, Berlin, February 20, 1943 (excerpt)

For the bureaucracy, deportation and killing of Jews became a mere administrative matter that had to be organizationally prepared, governed by regulations, and carried out accordingly.
Jurisdictions, category of persons affected, amount of luggage, guards for the transports, reports of orders carried out, final accounting of costs – everything was precisely stipulated. Only place and time had yet to be fixed.

■ *"During the period November 1 to December 4, the Security Police will deport 50,000 Jews from the Altreich [Germany within its 1937 borders], the Ostmark [formerly Austria], and the Protectorate of Bohemia and Moravia to the east in the vicinity of Minsk. The evacuation will be carried out using the Reichsbahn, with transport trains carrying 1,000 persons each"*

Directive of October 24, 1941, by Chief of General Police Kurt Daluege, to local police stations

2. Bielefeld, December 1941

In 1933, 903 Jews lived in Bielefeld, where a Jewish community had existed since the 114th century. Half of them were able to emigrate prior to the outbreak of war. How many subsequently fell into the hands of the

Gestapo is not known. Of 431 Jews from Bielefeld who were deported, only 31 survived until 1945. The photos document the first of seven transports from the administrative district of Minden, which left from Bielefeld station for Riga on December 13, 1941. Of the 400 persons deported that day, 47 survived, six of them from Bielefeld.

Deportation in Eisenach, May 9, 1942

■ *"SS first lieutenant Eichmann spoke first, by way of introduction, about the further evacuation of 55,000 Jews from the Altreich as well as the Ostmark and the Protectorate... The Jews must under no circumstances find out about the preparations for their evacuation; therefore, absolute secrecy is essential... There followed an exchange of information between agencies of the Gestapo that had already carried out evacuations, and others that are now facing what for them will be a new task."*

Report of a meeting of Section IV B 4, Reich Security Main Office, held on March 6, 1942

3. Organization and Implementation

Gestapo, Criminal and General Police, district administrators and mayors worked closely together to make sure everything went according to plan and the victims were "delivered on time by the policemen in charge." Every person about to be deported was issued a pamphlet with instructions to be followed under threat of punishment, as well as a question-

naire on which all property was to be entered.

Between November 1941 and June 1943, 4,744 Jews from the Franconia region were deported in six transports, among them 2,063 persons from Mainfranken. The transports went to Riga, Izbica, Theresienstadt, and Auschwitz. The number of those who survived is not known.

4. Würzburg, April 1942

Photo album of the Würzburg Gestapo

71

5. Reporting and Accounting

As the crimes were initiated on governmental authority, every operation had to be documented. Records, comments, and correspondence had to be filed according to date. A receipt gave the value of watches, clothing, and provisions confiscated during luggage control.

Also found here were a list of items confiscated by the Gestapo "for official use," a bill for renting a hall in an inn that served as an assembly point, and a deportee's last message home. For reference, see the files of the Nuremberg-Fürth State Police Office entitled: "Evacuation of Jews from Mainfranken (1941–1943)"

6. Hanau, Summer 1942

7. Reichsbahn Timetables

Auction of Jewish possession in Hanau, June 1942

The most important assistants to the Gestapo were the local administration and the police in the district from which the deportees came, the Reich Ministry of Transportation and the management of the German Railways, which provided "special trains for resettlement" to the ghettos and death camps.

The routes and dates were determined during special timetable conferences. These schedules had to be complied with by the local policemen who rounded up their Jewish neighbors. Jewish property went to the state; furniture and household items were auctioned off.

8. Siegburg, Summer 1942

The small synagogue congregation in Siegburg, near Bonn, that could look back upon 600 years of history, was likewise eliminated. 115 persons, approximately half of the congregation, emigrated during the years

1933 to 1939, the majority of them after the pogrom of 1938. In the summer of 1941, those who had remained behind were confined to a barrack camp in which they lived for another year.

The Jews from the entire district were deported east in four transports between June 14 and July 27, 1942. Of those whose names were known, only one survived.

The pictures are part of a series on the deportation of the Siegburg Jews taken by an unknown photographer at the assembly point, Brandstrasse 42–44. They show the ordered checking of luggage and the transport to the station.

9. An Example: The Netherlands

Wherever Hitler's armies marched in, officials of the Reich Security Main Office were immediately on the spot. Everywhere identical decrees were issued, identical measures carried out. Persecution started with public proclamations on registration, orders to wear the yellow star, the mounting of prohibitive signs, bans of profession, and confiscation of property.

Then, one day, "resettlement" began, as it was euphemistically termed. First, Jewish families were concentrated in certain buildings or city districts. Sooner or later, however, they were interned in a collecting camp, and finally transported to the east -- to an unknown destination.

10. Distinguishing Markings

■ "1. Jews who have reached the age of six are forbidden to appear in public without a Jewish star.
2. The Jewish six-pointed star, drawn in black lines, is made of yellow fabric the size of the palm of one's hand; the word 'Jew' is superimposed in black. It must be visibly displayed on the left side of the chest, firmly sewn to the piece of clothing."

Article 1 of a police instruction on distinguishing markings of Jews in Germany, dated September 1, 1941

Amsterdam

73

11. Amsterdam, Summer 1942

■ *"We project the initial transport, by mid July or beginning of August of this year, of about 40,000 Jews from occupied French territory, 40,000 Jews from the Netherlands, and 10,000 Jews from Belgium to the Auschwitz camp for deployment of labor; this is to be done in special trains carrying 1,000 persons each and running daily... I would appreciate you taking notice of this, and assume that on the part of the Foreign Office there will be no objections to this measure either".*

Eichmann, Reich Security Main Office, to Legation Secretary Rademacher, Foreign Office, dated June 22, 1942

● *"God and history will condemn us and declare us equally guilty of this mass murder if we keep silent now and look on. The Netherlands have been hard hit and deeply humiliated. Now we will have to prove that our honor has not been lost, our conscience not silenced, our faith not weakened under pressure... We ex-*

spect everyone who has the opportunity, especially officials, police, railway personnel, etc., to sabotage these sadistic Nazi measures."

Illegal Dutch pamphlet, July 1942

12. After the Roundup

Clandestine photo

The course of the deportations in the Netherlands was recorded in reports which Consul General Otto Bene, representative of the Foreign Office to the German Commissioner General, sent regularly to his ministry. The emerging picture is familiar from developments in other countries as well:

Initially, many of those called up still reported voluntarily for transports to "labor camps." But soon police had to be used to remove them from their apartments. Anyone able to do so went into hiding; others committed suicide. After initial protests, the Dutch population gradually settled down. There was collaboration as well as resistance. The

Security Police organized roundups to capture those who tried to escape. Nothing could stop the deportation program.

■ *"Regarding: Deportation of the Jews*
Deportation of the Dutch Jews proceeded undisrupted again this week. With the trains that departed today, 6,000 Dutch Jews have so far been deported. Deportation itself proceeded without incident, and it is not to be expected that the transports leaving in the coming weeks will encounter difficulties or disruptions."

The Reich Commissar for the occupied Dutch territories in the Hague, General Consul Otto Bene, in a secret report of July 31, 1942 to the Foreign Office in Berlin

■ *"Since my above-mentioned report, the situation has changed considerably. Since Jewry has discovered it and knows what is happening with the deportations and the labor details in the East, they no longer report to the weekly transports. Of 2,000 who were called up this week, only some 400 appeared. Those who were called up cannot be found in their homes. Thus it is difficult to fill the two trains, and we don't yet know how we will fill the trains in the coming weeks."*

Supplementary report by Reich Commissar, August 13, 1942

13. Hauled Away

14.

15. At the Assembly Point

● *"The undersigned Dutch Churches, already deeply disturbed by the measures taken against the Jews in the Netherlands which exclude them*

75

from participation in ordinary public life, were horrified to learn of the new measures by which men, women, children and entire families will be taken away and sent to Germany and to territories under its control.

The suffering thereby imposed upon tens of thousands, the awareness that these measures violate the deepest moral sentiments of the Dutch people and, above all, the intrinsic interference in what God has given us by way of law and justice compel the Churches to turn to you with the urgent plea that these measures not be carried out."

From a telegram by all Dutch Churches to the Reich Commissioner for the Occupied Dutch Territories, dated July 11, 1942

16.

17. From Westerbork to Auschwitz

Deportation trains left twice a week for Poland from the "police controlled transit camp" Westerbork in the Netherlands. The camp commandant, SS first lieutenant Gemmeker, had the processing of a transport recorded for posterity on film and in photographs.

■ *"The most important thing for me, now as before, is to see that as many Jews as humanly possible are dispatched to the East. In the brief monthly reports of the Security Police I want only to be informed about what has been carted off during the month, and what Jews are still left at this juncture."*

Heinrich Himmler, April 19, 1943

Chronology

1940

February 10–12	First deportations from the districts of Stettin, Stralsund and Schneidemühl to Lublin, Poland
April 9	*Germany invades Denmark and Norway*
May 10	*Germany invades Holland, Belgium, Luxembourg. Attack on France*
June 10	*Italy enters the war*
September 27	*Tripartite pact among Germany, Italy and Japan*
October 22	Deportation of 7,450 Jews from Baden, the Palatinate and the Saar region to southern France; they are sent to Auschwitz at the end of 1942

1941

February 13	Deportation of Viennese Jews ordered
March 24	*Start of German campaign in North Africa*
April 6	*Germany attacks Yugoslavia and Greece*
May 14	Mass arrest of 3,600 Jews in Paris
June 22	*Germany invades the Soviet Union*
July 31	Göring orders Heydrich to prepare the "Final Solution of the Jewish Question"
October 1	German Jews forbidden to emigrate
October 10	Heydrich makes Theresienstadt a ghetto camp
October 14	Start of general deportations from the Altreich
October 16	First deportations from the Protectorate
November 25	Decree on confiscation of the property of the deportees
December 7	*Japanese attack on Pearl Harbor; war with the USA*

1942

January 20	Wannsee Conference on the "Final Solution of the Jewish Question". Deportations to Theresienstadt begin
March 13	Decree on deportation of 110,000 Romanian Jews
March 28	First transports from Slovakia arrive at Auschwitz
March 30	First transports from Paris arrive at Auschwitz
April to July	"Resettlement" throughout Poland
May 27	Assassination of Heydrich in Prague
July 15	First deportation train from Holland to Auschwitz. Large-scale roundup in Paris
August 4	First deportations from Belgium to Auschwitz
August 18	First transport from Yugoslavia arrives at Auschwitz
August 26–28	7,000 "stateless" Jews arrested in non-occupied France
September 16	First major "resettlement" from Lodz ghetto completed (71,000 victims)
October 3	First major "resettlement" from Warsaw ghetto completed (310,000 victims)
October 28	First transport from Theresienstadt arrives at Auschwitz
November 7	*Allied landing in North Africa*
November 25	First deportations from Bergen, Norway to Auschwitz
December 10	First transport from Germany arrives at Auschwitz

1943

February 2	*German Sixth Army surrenders at Stalingrad*
February 27	Deportation of Jewish arms industry workers from Germany to Auschwitz ("Factory Operation")
March	Transports from Holland to Sobibor extermination camp; from Prague, Vienna, Luxembourg and Macedonia to Treblinka
March 15	Deportations from Saloniki and Thrace, Greece to Auschwitz
April 19	Bermuda Conference on immigration quotas for refugees from occupied Europe
July 9	*Allied landing on Sicily*
September 8	*Italy agrees to cease-fire with Allies*
September 11	Beginning of large-scale roundup in Nizza following occupation of southern France
September 26 to October 12	Danish resistance helps 7,500 Jews escape
October 18	First Rome-Auschwitz transport

8. The Countries of Deportations

Albania

Albania was incorporated into the Italian state system through military occupation in spring 1939. After the defeat of Yugoslavia in April 1941, the Kosovo region and the part of Montenegro predominantly settled by Albanians were added to it. After Italy's capitulation in 1943, German troops occupied the country. No information exists about either the number of Jews in Albania or their losses.

According to surviving German reports, over one thousand people were arrested. When the Germans marched into Kosovo in April 1941, they arrested 551 Jews. In April 1944, the SS Skanderbeg Division arrested 281 Jews in Pristina, and "510 Jews, Communists, Partisans and individual suspects" were arrested in May by the XXIst German Mountain Corps.

551 people were killed in the country itself, 530 were deported, and 104 ultimately returned from Bergen-Belsen.

Belgium

Prior to the war, roughly 90,000 Jews lived in Belgium, including 30,000 refugees from Germany. 8,000 continued their flight into France, where over half were subsequently arrested and deported to the extermination camps.

When, in October 1940, the German military commander directed the Jews to register, only 42,000 persons complied. Even among those, many went underground once the deportations began. Between August 4, 1942 and July 31, 1944, the Gestapo succeeded in deporting at least 25,450 people. Of those, 1,640 survived. The number of victims totals 28,518, including 5,430 children.

Antwerp

Bulgaria

At the outbreak of the Second World War, 48,000 Jews lived in Bulgaria. At the end of 1940, the Bulgarian government, which was allied with Germany, passed anti-Jewish legislation, but enforced it only reluctantly. When it was about to yield to German pressure in the matter of deportations, demonstrations were held, the churches protested, professional academic associations issued numerous statements of solidarity, and 42 members of parliament passed a protest resolution.

The government was forced to relent, and decided instead to use the Jews for forced labor in the provinces. In this way, all were saved. From Thrace and Macedonia, regions which Bulgaria had been forced to hand over to Greece and Yugoslavia after the First World War but was given back in 1941, 11,343 Jews were deported to Treblinka.

Denmark

Öresund (Baltic Sea)

In 1940, some 8,000 Jews lived in Denmark. Of these, 1,500 were refugees. As there was no occupation regime, the government was able to forestall anti-Jewish legislation and deportations for quite some time. The situation did not change until August 1943, when, in the face of mounting strikes and acts of sabotage, the Germans declared a state of emergency, depriving the Danish government of all authority and placing executive power in the hands of German troops stationed in the country.

Before mass arrests of Jews began, an employee of the German embassy, Georg Duckwitz, informed social democratic friends in the resistance movement. In an unprecedented rescue operation, 7,200 victims of Nazi persecution were first hidden and then ferried across the sound (Öresund) to safety in Sweden.

466 Jews were deported to Theresienstadt; yet even of those, all but 51 were saved through the intervention of the Danish government. Altogether, 116 Danish Jews perished.

Germany

In 1933, a little over half a million Jews lived in Germany; 80 % of them were German citizens. Many families had lived here for centuries. By the end of 1939, 362,737 Jews managed to emigrate. On October 1, 1941, before the deportations began, the official count was 165,582 Jews. Three years later, only 14,475 were left.

The German Jews had already faced eight years of persecution by the time they were deported to the East. They died in the ghettoes of Lodz and Theresienstadt, the execution trenches of Riga, Kovno and Minsk, and the gas chambers of the extermination camps. The total number of victims has been estimated at over 150,000.

Stuttgart

France

When the country surrendered in 1940, 330,000 Jews were living in France; of these, more than a third were stateless or refugees holding foreign passports.

Drancy, near Paris

The northern part of the country was occupied by the Germans, while the Vichy government controlled the unoccupied southern part. But German anti-Jewish legislation was introduced there too, with only a week's delay, and all foreign Jews were interned in both parts of the country.

In October 1940 Pétain government issued anti-Jewish decrees. Some of them exceeded the regulations of the Nuremberg Laws of 1935. In July 1942 the aryanization program was enfoced in to expropriate the French Jews. The Jewish property was conficated by the French government. At request of Laval, a member of the Pétain government, deportations had to include Jewish women and children to Auschwitz in 1942.

With the Allied landing in North Africa and the German occupation of southern France, the organized manhunt passed into German hands throughout the country. Between March 27, 1942 and August 15, 1944, 73,743 people were deported from France in 79 sealed transports. Among them were 4,000 youngsters under the age of 18, and 6,000 children under 13. Altogether, 75,670 people were deported, one third of them French citizens. There were 2,570 survivors. In France proper, at least 2,000 died in camps and over 1,000 were executed. The total number killed amounted to more than 76,000.

Greece

In 1941, when the Germans invaded, over 70,000 Jews lived in Greece. Deportations began in the German occupied zone and, after the capitulation of Italy in 1943, spread to those parts of the country that had until then been occupied by the Ita-

Thessaloniki

lians. They also included Crete, Corfu, and the Aegean Islands.

Many lives were saved by the solidarity of the population. The Greek Orthodox Church drew up many false baptismal certificates. With the aid of the resistance movement EAM/ELAS, thousands of young people were able to escape to liberated territory. Of 58,600 Jews who had been deported to Auschwitz, Treblinka and Bergen-Belsen, 2,200 survived. The oldest and largest community of Greek Jews in Thessaloniki, which once boasted 50,000 members, was almost completely annihilated.

Italy

In 1938, 57,000 native Jews and 10,000 refugees from Germany lived in Italy. 23,000 had emigrated by 1941. When the large-scale deportations began in 1942, the Fascist regime in Rome refused to cooperate. In both Italy and the Italian occupied zones of southern France, Yugoslavia, and Greece, Jews at first found themselves protected. The situation changed only in September 1943, after the Allied landing in Sicily, Mussolini's fall from power, and the occupation of northern Italy by German troops. In the city of Rome, with 8,000 Jews, all but 1,000 escaped deportation with the help of the local populace. Hundreds joined the partisans. 8,560 Jews were deported from Italy; only 1,009 returned at the end of the war.

Yugoslavia

Belgrade, Kalemegdan fortress

In April 1941, at the time of the German invasion, an estimated 82,000 Jews lived in Yugoslavia. Parts of the country were annexed by four neighboring states. What remained was Serbia, which was placed under German occupation law, and an "Independent State of Croatia," under the leadership of the clerical-fascist Ustaša regime.

Of the 17,000 Jews from Serbia and the Banat, all but 2,000, who had either gone underground or joined the Partisans, were killed, almost without exception in the country itself. Jewish men, together with Communists and Gypsies, were shot as hostages by army units, while women and children were asphyxiated in gas vans by the SS. Of the 39,000 Croatian Jews, 4,000 succeeded in escaping to the coastal region occupied by the Italians, 25,000 were killed in camps by the Ustaša, and another 10,000 were deported.

The total number of Jewish victims on Yugoslav territory was roughly 65,000. Of these, 4,000 were refugees from outside the country. 1,300 died as Partisans.

Luxembourg

Between 3,500 and 5,000 Jews lived in the Grand Duchy of Luxembourg in 1940, most of them refugees. Two thirds of them fled from the German invasion to the unoccupied zone of France, to Spain, or to Portugal. 674 Jews who remained in the "Gau Moselland," as the country was called after Germany annexed it, were deported. 58 survived. Altogether, at least 1,200 people were murdered.

The Netherlands

140,245 Jews lived in the Netherlands in January 1941. Of these, 118,455 were Dutch citizens, 14,493 refugees from Germany, and 7,297 of other nationalities. Between July 15, 1942 and September 13, 1944, 107,000 were deported to German concentration and extermination camps in 102 transports. Of these, 5,200 survived. With only a few exceptions, the names of those killed are known.

Westerbork

871 of the 56,500 deported to Auschwitz survived, as did 19 of the 34,313 deported to Sobibor. Only one person out of 1,700 deportees to Mauthausen survived. Approximately 20,000 people were saved by the Dutch resistance movement.

Norway

In April 1940, at the time of the German surprise attack, 1,800 Jews lived in Norway. Of these, 300 were refugees from Germany.

Oslo

At the end of October 1942, the German "Reich Commissioner" ordered the first arrests of Jews. The churches protested with announcements from the pulpit. The resistance movement hid hundreds of the persecuted, among them many elderly people and children, and smuggled them across the border into neutral Sweden.

759 men were deported to Auschwitz; of these, 25 survived. At least 758 were either executed or committed suicide in the country.

Austria

When the "Anschluss" took place in 1938, some 206,000 Jews lived in Austria. By the time emigration was prohibited in 1941, three quarters of them had left the country.

Initially, deportees were taken to Lodz, Riga, Minsk and Theresienstadt, and subsequently to the extermination camps. Nearly 49,000 were deported; barely 2,000 survived. If we add those who fled to other countries and were deported later from

Vienna

there, the number of Austrian victims totals 65,000.

Poland

The great majority of European Jews lived in Poland and the western areas of the Soviet Union, about three million of them in Poland. It was here that the policy of genocide claimed the greatest number of lives.

The Jews as a community suffered severe losses in all occupied countries of Europe, but in Poland they were virtually annihilated. Thousands were shot; tens of thousands perished in ghettos and camps. The

Warsaw

great majority died in the gas chambers of the extermination camps set up on Polish soil. The documentary records available do not allow a precise assessment of the number killed. On the basis of careful research, historians estimate the number to be at least 2.6 million.

Romania

750,000 Jews lived in Romania before the war. As a result of the forced cession of territory to the Soviet Union, Hungary, and Bulgaria in 1940, the number was reduced to 300,000. In 1941, the government joined Germany's war against the Soviet Union, reconquering Bessarabia and northern Bukovina and annexing the southern part of the Ukraine, which was renamed Transnistria.

The Romanian authorities organized bloody massacres and extensive deportations in the conquered territories, but, despite German pressure, refused to hand over their own citizens.

The toal number of victims of pogroms and mass executions and of those who perished as deportees in the ghettos and camps of Transnistria is at least 211,000 or, according to other estimates, 270,000.

The Soviet Union

Terezin

More than three million Jews lived in the Soviet Union before the Second World War. Here, the victims were for the most part shot on the spot or gassed in special vans. As a result of this particular German approach, no precise figures on number of victims exist. This is also the main reason why estimates of the total number of victims of genocide vary.

Fragmentary German documents account for at least one million killed in the Soviet Union, including the Baltic states. More recent studies have suggested a total of approximately two million victims.

Czechoslovakia

The Czechoslovak Republic, where thousands of refugees from Germany had found safety, was elimi-

nated when the Germans invaded in the spring of 1939. Bohemia and Moravia were declared a German Protectorate, while Slovakia became an independent state with a clerical fascist regime.

Of the 118,000 Jews living in the Protectorate, 26,000 were still able to emigrate, and 14,000 survived inside the country. The names of 77,279 victims, most of them deported to extermination camps via Theresienstadt, have been preserved.

Of the 89,000 Jews counted in Slovakia at the end of 1940, about 20,000 survived. Of the 57,000 deported to Auschwitz and Lublin, 300 returned. To these must be added 12,000 victims of other measures of persecution, which brings the figure to 69,000. The total number of losses for Czechoslovakia within its 1939 borders thus comes to 146,000 people

Hungary

Some 450,000 Jews lived in Hungary, which was allied with Hitler's Germany. As a result of territorial expansions at the expense of Czechoslovakia, Romania and Yugoslavia, this figure increased to an estimated 750,000 people.

Although the government in Budapest adopted Hitler's anti-Jewish legislation, it refused to hand over Jews with Hungarian citizenship to Germany. Not until the German armed forces had marched into Hungary in March 1944 was Eichmann able to begin operations there.

Among the first measures were marking with the yellow star and concentration in ghettos. To stay ahead of the Red Army, which was only 100 kilometers from the Hungarian border, the deportations were begun in the Carpathians and Transylvania, then extended to the entire country. In less than two months, 437,000 people were deported, and all but 20,000 survivors were killed in Auschwitz. And additional 106,000 people were deported to German concentration camps in November 1944; thousands perished on forced marches. Adding those who lost their lives in Hungarian work camps or otherwise died inside the country brings the total figure to more than half a million dead.

Budapest

Figure of Jewish victims in Europe (Borders of 1945)

Nördliches Eismeer

Atlantischer Ozean

Schweden

Finnland

Norwegen
>758

Helsinki

Leningrad

Oslo

Stockholm

Reval

Estland

Moskau

Riga

Lettland

Dänemark
116

Nordsee

Kopenhagen

Ostsee

Litauen

Wilna

Dublin

Irland

Minsk

Grossbritannien

Amsterdam

Niederlande
101 800

Berlin

Warschau

Sowjetunion
1 300 000 - 2 000 000

Kiew

London

Brüssel

Belgien
28 518

Deutschland
>150 000

Polen
2 600 000 - 3 000 000

Paris

Luxemburg
>1 200

Prag

Tschechoslowakei
146 000

Wien

Budapest

Odessa

Frankreich
>76 000

Schweiz

Österreich
>65 000

Ungarn
>500 000

Rumänien
211 000 - 270 000

Italien
7 551

Bukarest

Schwarzes Meer

Belgrad

Jugoslawien
65 000

Bulgarien
>11 000

Sofia

Istanbul

Madrid

Rom

Tirana

Albanien
977

Türkei

Spanien

Griechenland
56 400

Athen

Mittelmeer

9. The Transit Camps

Registration and marking of Jews was followed by their concentration, which preceded the deportations to death. In Western Europe, where no guarded ghettos like those in Poland and the Soviet Union were created, the victims were interned in collection camps for longer or shorter periods prior to deportation.

The majority of these camps had been built before the beginning of the war to hold refugees from Germany. In Holland, France, Hungary and Romania, they already existed before the German invasion. In Belgium, Italy and Yugoslavia, they were built later.

Most of these camps were in France. The earliest inmates were half a million refugees from Spain who sought asylum in this neighboring country after Franco's victory -- Spanish soldiers and civilians, as well as members of the International Brigades.

At the end of 1939, thousands of anti-fascists and all Jewish refugees from Germany and Austria were interned as "enemy aliens." After France's defeat, the French government utilized these places as collection centers for foreign Jews, who were later deported from there to the extermination camps in Poland. The camps became waiting rooms of death.

At first the camps were supervised by the Ministry of Defense, and after the capitulation by the Ministry of the Interior. The French police took over control of them from the military. Conditions were miserable almost everywhere. Bad food, too little drinking water, makeshift accommodations and primitive hygienic conditions were common to all of them. Epidemics broke out in some of the camps. Some 1,200 people died in Gurs alone. In some countries, the inmates' living conditions were better, but the same fate awaited all of them.

The names Westerbork and Hertogenbosch in the Netherlands, Malines in Belgium, Fossoli in Italy, Les Milles and Le Vernet, Rivesaltes and St. Cyprien, Compiègne, Pithiviers and Beaune-la-Rolande, Gurs and Drancy in France will forever be linked with the tragedy of European Jewry.

1. Roundup in Paris

In May 1941, the first 3,700 Jews were arrested in Paris and brought to the Pithiviers and Beaune-la-Rolande camps. By the end of the year, 9,000 people were interned.
Tens of thousands who had fled to southern France, later the "unoccupied zone," immediately after the German invasion and in subsequent weeks were also sent to internment camps.

Boulevard in Paris, August 20, 1941

2. Gurs and Le Vernet

In April 1939, the French government built the largest of numerous internment camps in Gurs, on the northern edge of the Pyrenees, 80 km. from the Spanish border. The earliest inmates were refugees from Spain. At the beginning of 1940, German emigrants were sent to the camp.
At the end of the year, they were followed by Jews deported from Germany. There were 30,000 internees, 10,000 of them women. In winter of

Le Vernet

1941–42, 800 prisoners died here of epidemics. Between August 1942 and autumn of 1943, 6,000 people were deported from Gurs via Drancy to Auschwitz and Sobibor.

3. Pithiviers and Beaune-la-Rolande

● *"Hygienic conditions can without exaggeration be described as unfit for human beings; there were few places to wash, which functioned only on occasion . . . and few toilets; long lines of impatient men tor-*

Beaune-la-Rolande

mented by dysentery formed in front of them from morning til evening curfew."

Alfred Kantorowicz,
interned at the Les Milles camp

■ "By the end of July, a total of 13,000 Jews had been evacuated from the occupied territory of France. By the end of August, 26,000 Jews will have left French soil... The transport schedule for the month of September also provides for 13 trains."

Notification from Gestapo Headquarters in Paris to the Chief of the General Staff of the Military Commander in France, July 30, 1942

4. Drancy and Les Milles

In August 1941, a complex of unfinished housing blocks in Drancy, near Paris, was turned into a collection camp for Jews. During the first two years, the camp was administered by the Paris police prefecture; in August 1943, it was taken over by the Gestapo.
Most of the Jews deported from France passed through this camp. On

Drancy

June 22, 1942 the first of 61 deportation trains left Drancy; the last departed on July 31, 1944. Over 62,000 people were deported from here to Auschwitz and Sobibor.

5. Deportation

Marseile, January 1943

■ "The Jewish children brought to the Pithiviers and Beaune-la-Rolande camps can be gradually distributed among the scheduled transports to Auschwitz. However, transports composed exclusively of children are on no account to be sent off."

Telex from the Reich Security Main Office to the commanders of the SIPO and the SD in Paris, August 13, 1942

■ "On August 14, 1942, transport train no. D 901/14 departed the Le Bourget-Drancy station for Auschwitz carrying a total of 1,000 Jews (including children for the first time). The persons involved were chosen in accordance with the guidelines that have been laid down."

Telex from Gestapo headquarters in Paris to the Reich Security Main Office and the Auschwitz camp on August 14, 1942

6. Theresienstadt Ghetto Camp

Small fortress

Theresienstadt, near Prague, served as a ghetto for elderly German Jews, who were sent to the "Reich Nursing Home" under "home purchase agreements," and as a transit camp for Jews from the "Protectorate of Bohemia and Moravia." In September 1942, well over 58,000 were herded together in an area where formerly 7,000 had lived; this included 30,000 elderly and sick people, nearly 4,000 invalids and over 1,000 blind people. Only 60 percent of the inmates had a place to sleep; 5,500 camped in lofts. There was one doctor for 1,500 patients. A total of 141,000 people were transported to Theresienstadt, including 70,000 elderly and 15,000 children. 33,550 died there. Between January 1942 and October 1944, 88,200 were deported to extermination camps, where all but 3,500 were murdered. 23,000 survived until liberation.

The Death Camps

The death camps were built on Polish territory. There the Jewish population of Poland was killed, as well as many deportees from Western Europe.

Chelmno, where the genocide began at the end of 1941 with three mobile gas vans, became a cemetery for the Jews of the Warta region. Between March and July 1942, additional extermination camps were built in Belzec, Sobibor and Treblinka. They were intended for "Operation Reinhard," as the extermination of the Jews from the Generalgouvernement was called after Reinhard Heydrich's death. Himmler put Odilo Globocnik, SS and Police Chief of the district of Lublin, in charge of the task. He had at his disposal a troop of 450 men, among them 92 "experts" who had already participated in the first "euthanasia" operation, the mass murder of over 70,000 sick and handicapped people in Germany.

In order to maintain the lie of "resettlement to the East," a region close to the eastern border of the *Generalgouvernement* was chosen. The camps were built at a safe distance from the nearest village, yet always adjoined a main railway line. All of them were equipped with stationary gas chambers, but lacked crematoria. Each housed a small German "Special Commando" *[Sonderkommando]* of 20 to 30 men, reinforced by 90 to 120 Ukrainian, Latvian or Lithuanian guards, and a work unit of several hundred Jews, who had to clear out the gas chambers, bury the dead, and collect their clothing and baggage. As they were witnesses, they too were killed after a few weeks and replaced by new arrivals.

Clearance of the ghettos proceeded with unprecedented brutality. The old and sick were shot on the spot. Operations always began without warning and usually lasted one or two days, though in the larger ghettos they could go on for several weeks. Transports from the districts of Cracow and Lemberg went to Belzec, those from Lublin to Sobibor, those from Warsaw and Radom to Treblinka. Frequently, the trains travelled for days. Many people died en route in the overcrowded freight cars. All others were killed immediately after their arrival.

After "Operation Reinhard" had been completed, Globocnik submitted to the Reichsführer SS, Heinrich Himmler, a final accounting of all proceeds yielded by this killing operation.

7. Deportation Experts

Dr. Albert Ganzenmüller (1905–1987), undersecretary in the Reich Ministry of Transport and deputy general director of the German Railways. Fled to Argentina after the war, returning in 1955. Prosecution begun in 1973, but dropped in 1977 because of his continuing unfitness to stand trial.

Karl Wolff (1900–1984),
SS lieutenant general and lieutenant general in the Waffen SS, Himmler's personal adjutant from 1933 on, head of his general staff beginning in 1936. Headed a public relations firm after the war. Arrested in 1962 and sentenced in 1964 to 15 years' imprisonment; early release in 1971 for good behavior.

Albert Ganzenmüller   Karl Wolff

"Since July 22, a train carrying 5,000 Jews has been leaving daily from Warsaw to Treblinka via Malkinia, and in addition, two times a week, a train with 5,000 Jews from Przemysl to Belzec. Gedob is in constant contact with the Security Service in Cracow. They agree that the trans-

ports from Warsaw to Sobibor (near Lublin) by way of Lublin should stop for as long as construction work on this stretch makes this transport impossible (approximately October 1942)."

Dr. Albert Ganzenmüller, Undersecretary in the Reich Ministry of Transportation and Deputy General Director of the German Railways, to SS Lieutenant General Karl Wolff, office of the Reichsführer SS, Heinrich Himmler, in a secret letter of July 28, 1942

"I sincerely thank you for your letter of July 28, 1942, also in the name of the Reichsführer SS. I was especially pleased to receive the information that for the last 14 days a train has been leaving daily for Treblinka with 5,000 members of the chosen people, and that in this way we are in a position to carry out this population movement at an accelerated tempo. I myself have made contact with the offices involved, so that smooth accomplishment of the entire measure appears to be guaranteed."

Wolff's response to Ganzenmüller from the Führer's headquarters, August 13, 1942

8. Chelmno

Guards at Chelmno

Chelmno (Kulmhof) was the first site at which facilities for mechanized mass murder were installed. Special closed trucks were used, into which motor exhaust fumes were directed. The killing trucks were used from December 1941 to April 1943, and again after June 1944. 152,000 Jews and 5,000 Gypsies were gassed here.

The victims came from the Lodz Ghetto and the Warta region, as well as Germany, Austria, and Czechoslovakia. In the Pabianice camp, Jewish prisoners were forced to sort the belongings of the victims. In order to hide the origins of the clothing, which was donated to the German Winter Relief, the yellow stars were removed.

9. Belzec

Belzec, on the Lublin-Lemberg railway line, was the site of the first of three extermination camps in which Jews from the *Generalgouvernement,* as well as deportees from other countries, were murdered. Between March and December 1942,

Guards at Belzec

over 600,000 people were suffocated with exhaust fumes. The bodies were buried in mass graves. In the first half of 1943, they were dug up and burned on a framework of railroad tracks. Afterwards, the camp was torn down and every trace removed. The Jewish work detail was brought to Sobibor and killed there.

10. Sobibor

Arrival of the deported

The Sobibor extermination camp, east of Lublin, went into operation in April 1942 and was already expanded in July. Initial transports came from Lublin, Warsaw and vicinity, and later from numerous European countries. The victims were suffocated with carbon monoxide. Their number is estimated at 250,000.

Starting in autumn of 1942, the SS began to open mass graves and burn corpses. On October 14, 1943, the Jewish resistance organization in the camp organized a revolt. Several hundred prisoners succeeded in breaking out. Most were shot, but fifty survived. The camp was razed.

11. Treblinka

Franz Stangl and Deputy Kurt Franz
(The photo come from the camp
commandant's album)

Treblinka was the third and last
camp erected for "Operation Reinhard," the extermination of the Jews
in the *Generalgouvernement*. The
facility resembled Sobibor in every
detail. It was built in June 1942 and
expanded in September. The number
of victims totaled 900,000.
Between July 23 and September 21,
1942, 366,000 Jews from Warsaw
and vicinity were killed. On August 2,
1943, prisoners in the Jewish work
detail organized a revolt and break-
out. Only 70 of the 700 who took
part succeeded in escaping.

12. Killing Specialists

Odilo Globocnik (1904–1945),
SS and police chief of the Lublin
district, was responsible for organization and execution of "Operation
Reinhard." Following his arrest by
British troops, he committed suicide
in May 1945.

Christian Wirth (1885–1944),
criminal investigator, was office manager of the killing facilities at Brandenburg, Hadamar and Hartheim
during the first "euthanasia" operation. Supreme commandant of Belzec, later inspector of the extermination camps. Shot in 1944 at Fiume by
Yugoslav partisans.

Odilo Globocnik   Christian Wirth

13. Final Report on "Operation Reinhard"

■ *"Valuables from operation "Reinhard" are to be delivered to the SS Main Office of Economic Administration, Berlin, to be forwarded to the Reichsbank or the Reich Ministry of Economics, as follows:*

a) Reichsmark amounts totalling
RM 53,013,133.51
b) Foreign currency in banknotes from all major countries of the earth (of which ½ million dollars are particularly important) totalling RM 1,452,904.65
c) Foreign currency in gold coins totalling RM 843,802.75
d) Precious metals (around 1,800 kilograms of gold and around 10,000 kg. of silver in bars) totalling RM 5,353,943.00
e) Other valuables such as jewelry, watches, glasses etc. (of which the number of watches given to the troop, around 16,000 usable and some 51,000 in need of repair, is to be particularly noted) RM 26,089,800.00

f) Some 1,000 wagons of cloth, totalling RM 13,294,400.00

Total: RM 100,047,983.91

Another 1,000 wagons of cloth are still in storage here, as well as some 50 % of the other valuables listed above, which must still be counted and assessed."

SS Major General Odilo Globocnik to Reichsführer SS Heinrich Himmler on November 4, 1943

10. Auschwitz

Late in the summer of 1941, Himmler designated Auschwitz as the central extermination and concentration camp of the Third Reich. Here, Jews, Gypsies and Soviet prisoners of war were systematically murdered. The original camp, built in 1940 for political prisoners, was expanded. Two additional camps were built at Birkenau and Monowitz. The construction work alone claimed the lives of 8,000 prisoners. Selections for the gas chambers began in the spring of 1942 at Birkenau. Simultaneously, construction projects for newer and larger killing installations were being prepared. They were completed during the first half of 1943. Genocide was being industrialized.

Four large-scale installations, gas chambers and crematoria of hitherto unknown proportions, all equipped with the latest technology, including electric freight elevators for transporting corpses, and using Cyclon B gas, turned Auschwitz-Birkenau into a gigantic death factory.

In 1944, a rail connection was laid into the camp proper, as if it were a factory. Freight trains delivered thousands of people and then carried their belongings to Germany. A work force of 700 prisoners was employed to sort them out. Cash went to the Reichsbank, clothing and shoes to the winter relief effort. Even hair, gold teeth, and ashes from the bones were utilized.

Those immediately killed upon arrival were the old and handicapped, anyone who wore glasses, pregnant women, and mothers with children. Healthy, strong young men and women who were chosen for forced labor by an SS physician were sent into the camp. In August 1944, 185,000 prisoners were held in three main camps and 40 satellite camps. Plans for the construction of additional killing facilities and an extension of the Birkenau camp to more than twice its size could not be implemented anymore.

The selection process at the ramp depended not only on the physical state of the deportees, but also on the camp's capacity and the manpower requirements at the time a transport arrived. During the summer months, when outside labor was in great demand, the percentage of those left alive was somewhat higher, while in winter it dropped. In every instance, however, the overwhelming majority of arrivals were killed at once. Moreover, of the 400,000 prisoners on the camp registration lists, only 60,000 were still alive when the war ended. The total number of victims in this place alone have been estimated at 1.5 million. With Auschwitz, the Nazi regime created its own, thoroughly fitting memorial.

1. Arrival

● *"The transport from Stettin to Auschwitz took three days and three nights. We were transported in cattle cars, approximately 45 people -- men, women and children -- to a closed car. During the entire three days and three nights we received nothing to eat and nothing to drink."*

Kai Feinberg, deportee from Norway

● *"When our car was finally opened, SS and prisoners in striped suits drove us out brutally, beating us with sticks, and chased us to the end of the ramp. The men were separated from the women and children; heart-rending scenes took place."*

Marc Klein, deportee from France

2. On the Ramp

● *"On March 8, 1943 I was arrested by the SS, along with my wife and three-year-old son, in the last mass operation against the Jews, and deported to the Auschwitz concentration camp, with my family, after several days in the Grosse Hamburger Strasse collection camp. When we arrived at the Auschwitz ramp I was separated from my wife and child, and have not seen them again since that day."*

Norbert Wollheim, deportee from Berlin

3. Lining up for "Selection"

4. Map of Auschwitz-Birkenau

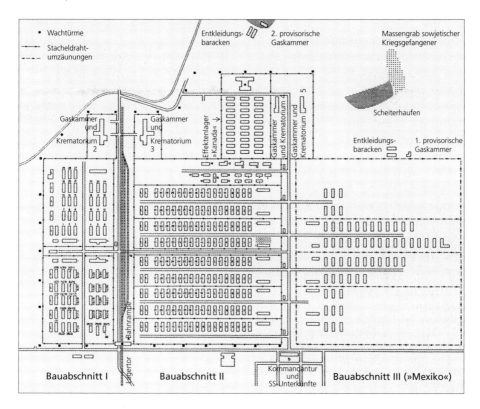

- Wachtürme
- Stacheldraht-
  umzäunungen

Entkleidungs-
baracken

2. provisorische
Gaskammer

Massengrab sowjetischer
Kriegsgefangener

Scheiterhaufen

Gaskammer
und
Krematorium
2

Gaskammer
und
Krematorium
3

Effektenlager
»Kanada«

Gaskammer
und Krematorium 4

Gaskammer und
Krematorium 5

Entkleidungs-
baracken

1. provisorische
Gaskammer

Bahnrampe

Lagertor

Kommandantur
und
SS-Unterkünfte

Bauabschnitt I

Bauabschnitt II

Bauabschnitt III (»Mexiko«)

Birkenau, originally planned as a prison of war camp, consisted of Section I (20,000 prisoners) and II (60,000 prisoners) to the left and right of the ramp, four large crematoria with underground gas chambers, and the "personal effects" area, where the clothes and luggage of the murdered people were sorted and prepared for transport to the Reich.

Section III, which was never completed, on the right side, and an additional Section IV on the left, not indicated on this map, were planned to hold another 60,000 prisoners each and increase the camp's capacity to 200,000. The course of the war prevented these plans from being carried out.

5. Auschwitz -- "Restricted Area"

The restricted area included a territory of 40 square kilometers that was constantly guarded by SS and police, and which Poles were forbidden to enter. The 1,600 people who had lived there were resettled and their village destroyed.

In this area were the main camp (Auschwitz I) and Birkenau (Auschwitz II). There were also extensive agricultural acreage and various factories, the administrative buildings and the guards' barracks. Monowitz and 40 smaller auxiliary camps (Auschwitz III) were located outside this area.

■ *"The way we selected our victims was as follows: Two SS doctors on duty in Auschwitz examined the arriving transports. The prisoners had to pass by a doctor, who signalled his decision as they walked by.*

Those fit to work were sent into the camp. Others were sent immediately to the extermination facilities. Children of tender years were exterminated without exception, as they were unable to work due to their youth."

The commandant of Auschwitz, Rudolf Höss, Cracow 1946

6. "Selection"

7.

● *"Scarcely fifteen minutes later, the chimney began to belch thick clouds of a black, sweetishsmelling smoke which bellied across the camp. A bright, sharp flame shot up six feet high. Soon the stench of burnt fat and hair grew unbearable.*

And still the lorries drove past, on the same route. We counted sixty batches that night... Soon after the last car had disappeared, the first lorries came back laden with the luggage and clothes of the dead, which they took to the depot."

Dr. Ella Lingens-Reiner, prisoner in Auschwitz

8. Two Directions

After the selection, the deportees were sent in different directions. The large majority went to the crematoria. The elderly and handicapped were brought there on trucks.

Only healthy young people who had been selected for slave labor went to the camp. In a few months, sick and unable to work, they would follow their families into death.

9. The Technology of Extermination

Most of the camp files were burned by the SS before the end of the war. Among the documents that chanced to survive were also some regarding the construction of the new Crematoria II and III in the winter of 1942–43.

Four large crematoria were completed by the summer of 1943. When the transports from Hungary arrived in summer of 1944, their daily capacity of 8,000 murdered people was further increased by burning corpses outdoors.

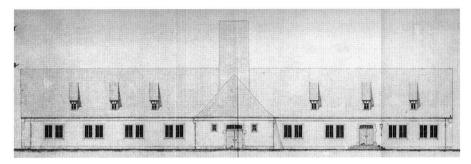

Architectural drawing of crematorium II, January 15, 1942.

■ *"Despite unspeakable difficulties and frost, crematorium II was completed, including construction details, using all available labor through day and night operation. The ovens were fired up in the presence of the inspecting chief engineer of the constructing firm, Topf & Sons, Erfurt, and they functioned flawlessly. As a result of frost, the reinforced concrete ceilings of the mortuary could not yet be built. However, this is insignificant, as the gassing cellar can be used for this. As a result of a train blockage, the firm Topf & Sons could not deliver the ventilation systems on time, as requested by the central site supervisor. However, once the ventilation systems arrive, installation will begin immediately, so that the facility should be completely operational on February 20, 1943 . . ."*

The Auschwitz head site supervisor, SS Captain Bischoff, to the chief of Amtsgruppe C, SS Captain Dr. Kammler, SS Main Office of Economic Administration, Berlin, on January 29, 1943

10. The Administration of Death

The changing euphemisms on the permits to collect Cyclon B inadvertently indicate the use made of this chemical. The breakdown on selections from the transports is also unmistakable.

It was noted exactly how many of the deportees were "accommodated separately," that is, immediately gassed, and how few were sent to the camp for forced labor. Even the hair of the victims was industrially "utilized."

(see also pp. 105/106)

11. Clandestine Report

Burning bodies outdoors

● *"We are sending you photos of a gassing operation in Birkenau. One photo shows an outdoor pyre on which corpses are burned because the crematorium cannot keep up. In front of the pyre lie corpses to be added to the pile.*
The other picture shows one of the sites in the woods where people undress, supposedly for the baths, before they go to the gas.
Urgent: send us two rolls of film for a 6 x 9 camera as quickly as possible. It is possible to take more photos."

Message from the camp resistance organization, smuggled out of Birkenau along with the photographs

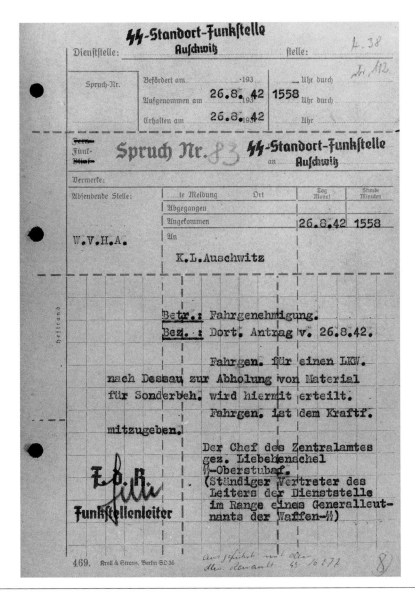

SS-Standort-Funkstelle
Auschwitz

Dienststelle: _____ stelle: _____ L.38

_____ Tr.112

Spruch-Nr.	Befördert am _____ -193___ _____ Uhr durch _____
	Aufgenommen am **26.8.42** **1558** Uhr durch _____
	Erhalten am **26.8.**19**42** _____ Uhr _____

Fern-
Fun- **Spruch Nr. 83** **SS-Standort-Funkstelle**
Blin- an **Auschwitz**

Vermerke:

Absendende Stelle:	_____te Meldung	Ort	Tag Monat	Stunde Minuten
	Abgegangen			
	Angekommen		26.8.42	1558
W.V.H.A.	An			
	K.L.Auschwitz			

Betr.: Fahrgenehmigung.

Bez.: Dort. Antrag v. 26.8.42.

Fahrgen. für einen LKW.
nach Dessau zur Abholung von Material
für Sonderbeh. wird hiermit erteilt.
Fahrgen. ist dem Kraftf.
mitzugeben.

Der Chef des Zentralamtes
gez. Liebehenschel
SS-Oberstubaf.
(Ständiger Vertreter des
Leiters der Dienststelle
im Range eines Generalleut-
nants der Waffen-SS)

Funkstellenleiter

469. Kroll & Straus, Berlin SO 36

aus geführt mit dem
dem Renault SS 16272 (8)

"Re: Drivers License
Ref.: Application of August 26, 1942

Permission to drive a truck to Dessau to pick up material for special treatment is hereby granted. The drivers permit is to be given to the driver."

SS Lieutenant Colonel Liebehenschel, SS Main Office of Economic Administration, Berlin, to Auschwitz concentration camp. Radio message no. 83 on August 26, 1942.

Driver's permit to pick up Cyclon B from Dessau

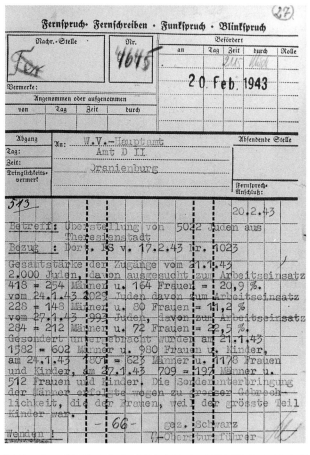

"Re: Transfer of 5,022 Jews from Theresienstadt

Total size of arrivals on January 21, 1943
2,000 Jews; of that, selected for work detail
418 = 254 men and 164 women = 20.9 %
on January 24, 1943, 2,029 Jews, of that, for work detail,
228 = 148 men and 80 women = 11.2 %
On January 27, 1943, 993 Jews, of that, for work detail,
284 = 212 men and 72 women = 22.5 %
On January 21, 1943, accommodated separately:
1582 = 602 men and 980 women and children
on January 24, 1943, 1801 = 623 men and 1178 women and children,
on January 27, 1943 709 = 197 men and
512 women and children. Special accommodation of the men occurs due
to too-great frailty, and of the women because the majority were children."

Telex from SS First Lieutenant Schwarz, Auschwitz, to the Main Office of Economic Administration, Oranienburg, on February 20, 1943

Report on selections from transports at Auschwitz

12. Between Two Transports

● *"The transport I saw consisted of Polish Jews. They had not received water for days. When the doors of the freight cars were opened, we were ordered to drive them out with loud shouts. They were completely exhausted, and approximately a hundred had died on the journey. The survivors had to line up in fives. It was our job to remove the bodies, the dying, and the luggage from the cars.*

The bodies (and these included anyone who could no longer stand up) were stacked in a heap. Pieces of luggage and packages were collected and piled up. Then the railroad cars had to be thoroughly cleaned so that no trace of their horrible load remained."

Report by a prisoner

14. Condemned to Death

■ *"For obvious reasons, the Auschwitz camp has again requested that no type of unsettling revelations be made to the Jews before deportation on what lies ahead of them. I request acknowledgement and compliance. In particular, I request that escort commandos be regularly instructed not to give any hints whatsoever to the Jews during the trip that would lead to resistance, or to speculate on the kind of accommodation, etc. In the interests of accomplishing urgent schemes plans, Auschwitz must insist on being able to receive the transports and assign them further with the least possible friction!"*

Telex from the Reich Security Office to the commanders of the SIPO and the SD in the Hague, Paris, Brussels and Metz, April 29, 1943

13.

15.

16. A Gas Chamber

Auschwitz I

17. A Crematorium

Crematorium II, Birkenau

■ *"When I built the extermination building at Auschwitz, I used Cyclon B, a crystallized prussic acid, which we threw into the death chamber through a small opening. It took 3 to 15 minutes, depending on climatic conditions, to kill the people in the death chamber. We knew when the people were dead because they stopped squealing.*
We normally waited a half an hour before opening the doors and re-moving the corpses. After the corpses were taken away, our special work details took off their rings and pulled the gold from the teeth of the bodies."
The commandant of Auschwitz, Rudolf Höss, Cracow 1946

18. Storeroom for Shoes

■ *"You will recall the Reichstag session in which I declared: If Jewry imagines it can engineer an international world war to exterminate the European races, the result will be not the extermination of the European races, but the extermination of Jewry in Europe (applause).*
They always laughed at me as a prophet. Of those who used to laugh, many are no longer laughing (scattered laughter, applause). Those who are still laughing now, soon may not be laughing anymore (laughter, heavy applause). This wave will sweep beyond Europe to cover the whole world."
Adolf Hitler on November 8, 1942

19. "Camp Canada" --
   Sorting Personal Effects

Clothes of the victims

■ *"By 1942, Canada I could no longer keep up with the sorting. Despite constant addition of sheds and barracks, day and night sorting by prisoners, and continual reinforcement of the work details, the unsorted luggage piled up, although numerous cars, often as many as twenty a day, were loaded with sorted mate-rial. In 1942, construction began on Personal Effects Camp Canada II, on the western edge of Section II of Birkenau. ... The thirty barracks had hardly been erected before they were already full. Mountains of unsorted luggage piled up between them."*

The commandant of Auschwitz, Rudolf Höss, Cracow 1946

Luggage of a transport

Chronology

1940

April 30	Auschwitz concentration camp built
June 14	First prisoner transport arrives

1941

January	Dr. Otto Ambros, board member of IG Farben, views the location for construction of the Buna factory
March 1	Himmler inspects Auschwitz and orders it be expanded to hold 30,000 prisoners. A camp for 100,000 prisoners of war is to be built at Birkenau
July 29	Himmler orders that Birkenau be turned into an extermination camp
September 3	First experimental gassing of 600 Soviet POWs and 300 sick prisoners with Cyclon B
October 8	Construction begins at Birkenau
December 7	Chelmno extermination camp built

1942

January 20	The Wannsee Conference: plans for the murder of 11 million people
January	First gassings in Birkenau
March 17	Belzec extermination camp erected. "Operation Reinhard" begins
March 26	First Reich Security Main Office transport arrives carrying Jewish deportees
April 1	Of 28,645 registered prisoners in Auschwitz-Birkenau, 10,629 are still alive; of 11,000 Soviet POWs, only 365
May 4	First selections in Birkenau camp
May 7	Sobibor extermination camp erected
May 12	First mass gassing in Auschwitz (1,500 victims)
July 17	2nd inspection tour of Auschwitz by Himmler
July 22	Treblinka extermination camp erected
Autumn	Maidanek concentration camp becomes an extermination camp
October 4	Himmler orders deportation of all Jewish prisoners from concentration camps in Germany to Auschwitz and Maidanek
December 1	Number of prisoners in Auschwitz-Birkenau: 30,623. 53,665 prisoners have died since April 1
December 17	The Allies solemnly promise to avenge the extermination of the Jews
December 28	Professor Clauberg begins his sterilization experiments

1943

February 22	Total number of prisoners in Auschwitz and auxiliary camps: 73,669
February 26	"Gypsy family camp" set up in Birkenau
March 8	Krupp concern decides to set up a factory in Auschwitz
May 4	First bombardment of industrial plants near Auschwitz
June 25	Last of four large new crematoria completed in Auschwitz-Birkenau
November 22	Auschwitz concentration camp divided into three independent camps with a common administration: Auschwitz I (original camp), Auschwitz II (Birkenau), Auschwitz III (auxiliary camps)

1944

April	First transports of Jewish concentration camp prisoners back to Germany for forced labor in the arms industry
April 14	First photos of Auschwitz by Allied reconnaissance planes
May 15–July 9	Deportation of 437,000 Jews from Hungary to Auschwitz
August 1	"Gypsy camp" dissolved; 4,000 people gassed

11. Life in a Concentration Camp

Innumerable camps of every kind, category and size existed in Hitler's occupied Europe: labor camps, transit camps, prisoner of war camps, and concentration camps with countless satellite camps, all of which held political prisoners from every European country. Such names as Dachau, Sachsenhausen, Buchenwald, Flossenbürg and Mauthausen, Ravensbrück, Natzweiler, Neuengamme, Stutthof and Gross-Rosen have become synonymous with horror. In addition, there were the extermination camps, where no human beings lived except for the German guards and a Jewish work unit. Only two combined concentration-extermination camps existed: Maidanek near Lublin, and the infamous Auschwitz-Birkenau.

The selection process did not make the choice between life and death, but merely determined the time of death. Most were killed at once; the rest were exploited through forced labor to the point of total physical exhaustion. In the language of the SS, this was called "annihilation through labor." The German Reich hired out its slaves for three to four Reichsmarks a day to numerous industrial concerns. By the end of 1944, this was bringing in an income of over 50 million Reichsmarks a month.

Daily routine in the camps was marked by completely insufficient nutrition and clothing, catastrophic sanitary conditions, roll calls lasting for hours in every kind of weather, and inhumane treatment by the guards. Barbaric disciplinary punishments, ranging from deprivation of food, cells too small to sit down in, and whipping, to the gallows, created an atmosphere of constant terror. In the hierarchy of prisoners, Jews occupied the lowest rung.

After three to six months at the latest, a prisoner had usually reached the end of his strength. If he did not die or, in despair, commit suicide, he was found unsuitable for work during one of the dreaded "follow-up selections," and either killed by an injection of carbolic acid or sent to the gas chamber. Only those able to secure jobs in the camp administration, the infirmary, or the kitchen had a chance of survival. More than a million people of all nationalities died in the concentration camps.

SS camp physicians not only carried out selections of entire trainloads of people for the gas chambers and supervised public beatings and executions. They also conducted long-term medical experiments on living human beings for military purposes, for "racial hygiene" research, and for the pharmaceutical industry. These experiments also took many lives.

In October 1942, Himmler issued an order that all concentration camps in Germany be made "free of Jews." But the precarious situation of the German war economy in the spring of 1944 forced the SS to return Jewish prisoners to Germany to work in the armaments industry.

1. An Alien World

SS guards

The newcomer to the camp entered an alien world with laws of its own. He was robbed of his civilian clothing and all personal belongings, his hair was cut off and he was given the uniform of a prisoner. A number was tattooed onto his arm, which replaced his name from then on.

His previous life was obliterated. He had no rights; he was subject to the iron discipline of camp regulations and the terror of camp guards, and exposed to hunger and cold. A merciless struggle to stay alive began that very few could survive.

2. Forced Labor

● *"A work detail of 100 men lost around 10 prisoners daily. The prisoners died from undernourishment, accidents, etc. Food was bad and clothing insufficient. . . . There were no washing facilities or soap with which to clean clothes. The clothes I distributed came from those gassed in Birkenau."*

Noack Treister, prisoner in Auschwitz

● *"How long could death be postponed? In Birkenau, prisoners in work details could count on two to three months . . . a beating by an SS man, a blow from a club was enough to finish them off, so they would inevitably be taken at the next "selection."*

Robert Levy, prisoner in Auschwitz

3. Himmler at Auschwitz

On July 17, 1942, SS Leader Heinrich Himmler visited Auschwitz for the second time. In Monowitz he viewed the site of IG Farben's Buna factory, still under construction, and was advised of the progress of the work by Chief Engineer Faust.

Earlier, in Birkenau, in the presence of camp commandant Rudolf Höss, he had taken part in the selection, gassing and cremation of a transport of deportees in order to become familiar with the procedure.

The photographer did not capture this on film.

Himmler at Monowitz, July 17, 1942

4. IG Farben

■ *"Enclosed please find the report on our construction discussions... On the occasion of a dinner given by the concentration camp administration, we decided upon all measures regarding utilization of the truly excellent functioning of the concentration camp for the benefit of the Buna factory."*

Dr. Otto Ambros, IG Farben board member, to the management of the concern, April 12, 1941

Buna plant, Monowitz

■ *"According to my recollection, concentration camp prisoners were employed in almost all German industries in which mass employment was possible.... In all of German industry, at the peak of this employment, some 500,000 concentration camp inmates were utilized."*

SS Lieutenant Colonel Karl Sommer, SS Economic Administration Office

(see next page)

5. Krupp, Siemens-Schuckert, Rheinmetall, Borsig et al.

■ *"We at Krupp never worried much about life. We simply wanted a system that functioned well and gave us the opportunity to work undisturbed. Politics is not our concern....*

When I was asked what I knew about the Nazis' anti-Jewish policies, I said that I did not know about the extermination of the Jews, and in addition: when you buy a good horse, you have to accept a few shortcomings."

Alfried Krupp von Bohlen und Halbach, 1945

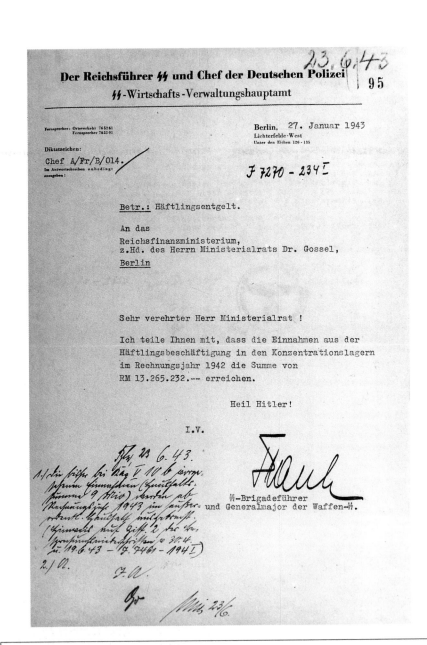

Der Reichsführer ✠ und Chef der Deutschen Polizei

✠-Wirtschafts-Verwaltungshauptamt

Fernsprecher: Ortsverkehr 765261
Fernsprecher 765101

Berlin, 27. Januar 1943
Lichterfelde-West
Unter den Eichen 126-135

Diktatzeichen:

Chef A/Fr/B/014.

Im Antwortschreiben unbedingt
anzugeben!

F 7270 - 234 I

Betr.: Häftlingsentgelt.

An das
Reichsfinanzministerium,
z.Hd. des Herrn Ministerialrats Dr. Gossel,
Berlin

Sehr verehrter Herr Ministerialrat !

Ich teile Ihnen mit, dass die Einnahmen aus der
Häftlingsbeschäftigung in den Konzentrationslagern
im Rechnungsjahr 1942 die Summe von
RM 13.265.232.-- erreichen.

Heil Hitler!

I.V.

✠-Brigadeführer
und Generalmajor der Waffen-✠.

Re: Prisoner payment

"I would like to inform you that income from prisoner labor in the concentration camps came to a sum of 13,265,232.00 Reichsmarks in fiscal year 1942."

SS Brigade Leader Frank, SS Main Office of Economic Administration, to Assistant Secretary Dr. Gossel, Reich Finance Ministry, on January 27, 1943

6. Living Arrangements

Latrine

▲ "In the men's camp at Birkenau there were only three toilet barracks for thirty-two living barracks. Since an average of 30 percent of all prisoners suffered from diarrhea due to starvation, this small number of toilets was completely inadequate. Guards made sure that these toilet facilities could only be used for a very short period. ... There was no toilet paper."

From the indictment in the first Auschwitz trial, Frankfurt 1963

▲ "The roofs of the barracks were not water-tight. In bad weather, the rain came in at many places. The three-story wooden bunks were lined only with straw, which became dirty and dusty or was wet through. Sometimes there was no straw at all. Then the prisoners slept on the bare boards."

From the verdict of the Frankfurt 1965 court in the first Auschwitz trial

7. Roll Call

● "At 3:30 in the morning the shouting of the guards woke us up and with cudgel blows we were driven from our bunks to go to roll call. Nothing in the world could release us from going to the roll call; even those who were dying had to be dragged there. We had to stand there in rows of five until dawn."

Marie Claude Vaillant-Couturier, prisoner in Auschwitz

■ "The roll call, held twice daily, required the prisoners to stand for hours in the wet, cold, and mud. If it had rained during the day, the prisoners had to lie in the bunks at night in their wet clothing. It was no wonder that hundreds died each day."

SS Corporal Pery Broad, Auschwitz political department

Auschwitz

8. Experiments on Human Beings

SS Captain Dr. Sigmund Rascher and the director of the Institute of Aviation Medicine, Siegfried Ruff, carried out medical experiments for the German air force on prisoners from Dachau concentration camp. Approximately 170 died as a result. One of those experiments was exposure to icy water.

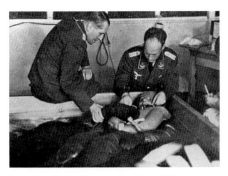

Exposure to iced water, Dachau 1943

■ *"For such a series of experiments, Auschwitz is better suited in every respect than Dachau, as it is colder there, and because of its size, less attention is roused in the camp itself (the experimental subjects yell (!) when they freeze)."*

SS captain and medical doctor Rascher to Reichsführer SS Heinrich Himmler on February 17, 1943

9.

In another series of experiments, Dr. Rascher locked the prisoners in low-pressure chambers that simulated heights of up to 20,000 meters. Here, too, the death of the subjects was not only accepted, but was itself part of the experiment. Other SS doctors infected their victims with malaria, spotted fever and gas burns, burned them with phosphorous, and attempted bone transplants.

10. The Doctors

At Himmler's behest, Professor Carl Clauberg, head physician at the Königshütte Gynecological Clinic, tested a sterilization procedure on Jewish and Gypsy women in Auschwitz and Ravensbrück. Many of the women died. Clauberg, sentenced by the Soviet Union in 1948 to 25 years imprisonment, was released to West Germany in 1955 under the "returnee" arrangement between Bonn and Moscow. He was arrested again, but died shortly before his trial.

11.

An example of the causal link between inhuman science and criminal practice was the Kaiser Wilhelm Institute for Anthropology, Human Genetics and Eugenics in Berlin. Its director, Prof. Eugen Fischer, who had paved the way theoretically for Nazi racial policies, worked closely with the SS and the Reich Geneology Office after 1933.

Otmar von Verschuer

In 1942, he was succeeded by his student, Prof. Otmar Freiherr v. Verschuer, known for research on twins. A year later, Verschuer's earlier assistant, Dr. Josef Mengele, became the Auschwitz camp doctor.

12. Children as Guinea Pigs

Josef Mengele

In Auschwitz, with Himmler's permission, Mengele worked on a research project of Verschuer that was financed by the German Society for Research. He infected twin children with typhus and later had them killed. The preserved organs were sent to his supervisor in Berlin.

In 1945, Verschuer destroyed all incriminating evidence and continued his career at the University of Münster. Mengele escaped to South America, where he died in 1979. Fischer became honorary president of the German Anthropological Society in 1953.

13. Punishments

With music to the gallows, Mauthausen

● *"There were always public hangings, on an average of two to three a week. The reasons were trivial. I remember the case of a young Frenchman shortly before his seventeenth birthday. In order to have some sort of celebration, he tried to obtain a piece of bread and a half a jar of jam. He was caught by the SS and hanged."*

Grégoire Afrine, prisoner in Auschwitz

The SS sent trainloads of people to the gas chambers without asking their names. The guards' power over the prisoners allowed all sorts of arbitrary behavior. But the files of the camp bureaucracy make even open terror seem correct and legal.

14. "Departures"

Belsen (Sandborstel)   Sachsenhausen

● "Selections occurred every 3–6 weeks, as well as in the hospital at Monowitz, on the roll call field and at the Monowitz gate when the prisoners left. The selected prisoners were thrown onto open trucks -- without shoes or underclothes (even in winter) -- and taken away."

Leon Staischak, former prisoner, at the Nuremberg trials

● "The index of the dead was far larger than that of the living. I estimate -- and I repeat that I was head of the orderly room for a long time -- that the number of the living at Buna (Monowitz) at the end was 10,000 prisoners, while the number of dead was 120,000, and the total number of the living in the auxiliary camps 35,000, while the approximate number of deaths was 250,000."

Dr. Gustav Herzog, former prisoner, at the Nuremberg trials

15. "New Arrivals"

Auschwitz-Birkenau

12. The Warsaw Ghetto Uprising

The Jews were not merely passive victims. Defenseless as they were, they still fought back, wherever, however, and for as long as they could, though they did so under far more difficult circumstances than other resistance groups in occupied Europe. Since their physical annihilation was the objective of Nazi policy, every move they made in their struggle for survival, every violation of the laws directed against them and their right to exist, became acts of resistance.

An illegal press developed in Warsaw and Cracow to supply the ghetto population with information. In private homes, entire school classes prepared for their final exams. Ghetto dwellers organized the smuggling of food, clothing, medical supplies, and subsequently even weapons. Activists from different parties in the ghettos joined to form underground organizations, from which the first combat groups later evolved.

In April 1943, the largest armed uprising broke out in the Warsaw Ghetto, when those who had survived the deportations of the previous summer and had been protected as factory workers were to be taken away with their families. The fighting, which the SS estimated would last for three days, continued for nearly a month. Three months after the defeat at Stalingrad, victory was won here over 56,000 civilians -- men, women, and children -- with machine guns, flamethrowers, mortars, and field artillery.

Armed uprisings also took place in the ghettos of Bialystok, Vilna, Czestochowa, Cracow, and numerous other places. Even in the death camps of Sobibor and Treblinka, there were skirmishes with the SS and attempted breakouts. Prisoners even blew up a crematorium in Auschwitz-Birkenau.

Most of those who succeeded in fleeing from the ghettos and camp, escaping mass executions, or jumping from deportation trains joined the partisans in the forests. In southern and eastern Europe, wherever geographic conditions permitted, armed struggle went on. In western Europe, resistance concentrated on providing Jewish refugees with forged papers, finding them hiding places, and helping them escape to neutral countries.

Over one million Jewish men fought as soldiers with the Allied armies. But the symbol of Jewish resistance remains the Warsaw Ghetto Uprising, an event which the SS immortalized with an illustrated report for their own glorification.

1. Defenders of the Ghetto

● *"Arise, people, and fight for your lives!*
Every mother should become a lioness, defending her children!
Fathers, stop watching you children die! ...
May each house become a fortress! Arise, people, and fight! Salvation lies in the struggle. Those who fight for their lives have a chance to save themselves. We rise in the name of the struggle and the lives of the helpless who we wish to save."

From an illegal appeal, January 1943

2. The Battle Begins

■ *"Before the beginning of this large-scale operation, the borders of the former Jewish district were sealed off with an external barrier ... In the first penetration into the ghetto, the Jews and Polish bandits*
succeeded in repulsing the forces involved, including tanks and armored cars, through a planned attack."

Final report by SS and Police Chief Jürgen Stroop

● *"A few hours ago, SS units armed with tanks and artillery began murdering the remaining population of the ghetto. The ghetto is resisting bitterly and heroically. The Jewish Fighting Organization is leading the defense ... Of course, the outcome of the battle is clear from the outset."*

Telegram to London from the Jewish Fighting Organization (ZOB), April 19, 1943

3. "Relocation" of the Factories

4. Arrest of Workers

■ *"After the first few days I realized that the original plan could not be carried out if the armaments and defense industry factories scattered throughout the ghetto were not dissolved. Therefore, it was necessary to demand that these factories be cleared and immediately relocated by a suitable deadline. One factory after another was dealt with in this way....*

On April 23, 1943, an order came from the Reichsführer SS through the Higher SS and Police Chief East in Cracow to comb the ghetto in Warsaw with the greatest possible severity and merciless tenacity. I therefore decided to begin the total destruction of the Jewish district by burning down all housing blocks, including the housing blocks near the armaments factories."

Final report by SS and Police Chief Jürgen Stroop

5. Leap to Death

● *"In the houses, thousands of women and children were burned alive. Horrible screams and cries for help could be heard from the burning houses. People appeared in the windows of many houses engulfed in flames, like living torches."*

Report no. 5 by the Jewish Fighting Organization (ZOB)

■ *"In groups -- whole families -- the Jews, already caught by the flames, jumped from the windows or tried to lower themselves on sheets etc. knotted together. Measures were taken so that these, as well as other, Jews were immediately liquidated."*

Daily report by the SS and Police Chief on April 22, 1943

6. The Commander of the Ghetto liqudation forces

■ *"From one complex of buildings, the team involved in cordoning off the area was even shot at. A special unit was brought in, and all buildings were set afire in order to smoke out the bandits. The Jews and bandits held out until the last moment, and then fired on the men in the unit. Shooting occurred even with carbines. A number of bandits shooting from balconies were shot down."*

Daily report by SS and Police Chief on April 23, 1943

8. Two Appeals

● *"Poles, citizens, soldiers of freedom! Amidst the thunder of artillery with which the German army is bombarding our houses and apartments, our mothers, children and wives; amidst the clatter of machine guns we have captured in combat with the gendarmes and SS; amidst the smoke of the conflagration, from a sea of blood of the Warsaw Ghetto, we prisoners of the ghetto send you fraternal battle greetings.*
...

It is a struggle for our freedom and yours, for our human, social, and national honor and dignity and for yours. We avenge the crimes of Auschwitz, Treblinka, Belzec and Maidanek.

Long live the comradeship in arms of fighting Poland! Long live the life and death struggle against the occupiers!"

Appeal from the Jewish Fighting Organization (ZOB), April 23, 1943

(see next page)

7.

9. "Pulled from Bunkers"

"Stop! Restricted Area!
Entering the former Jewish residential quarter is strictly forbidden.
Anyone found in the former Jewish residential quarter without a new, valid identity card will be shot.
All identity cards issued before 23 April 1943 permitting entry into the former Jewish residential quarter are no longer valid."

Announcement by the SS and Police Chief in the District of Warsaw, Jürgen Stroop, SS and Police Brigadier General, April 23, 1943

Order by the "Leader of the Large-Scale Operation" on April 23, 1943

10. Captured Fighters

■ *"It becomes ever clearer that the toughest, most resistant Jews and bandits are now left. Many bunkers have been opened by force whose occupants had not been to the surface since the beginning of the operation. In a number of cases, after the bunker was blown open the occupants were hardly able to creep to the surface."*

Daily report by the SS and Police Chief, April 26, 1943

● *"We are already in the eighth day of the life and death struggle ... The number of victims, that is, victims of shootings and of the fires in which men, women and children have been killed, is enormous. Our final days are approaching. But as long as we are able to hold weapons in our hands, we will continue to resist and to fight."*

Report by the Jewish Fighting Organization (ZOB), April 26, 1943

11.

■ *"In the measures taken today, 1,026 Jews were captured, 245 of them killed in battle or resistance. The Jews captured today were all removed from the bunkers through force. No voluntary abandonment of the opened bunkers was recorded today. A large number of captured Jews was taken from the sewers. Systematic blasting or burial of sewer exits continues."*

Daily report by SS and Police Chief, May 1, 1943

■ *"Resistance by the Jews continued unabated today. In contrast to previous days, the remaining members of the main Jewish battle group who have not yet been exterminated apparently retreated to the highest ruins they could reach, in order to cause the commandos on duty losses by shooting."*

Daily report by SS and Police Chief, May 10, 1943

12. "Shock Troops"

13. To the "Umschlagplatz" transit point

■ *"The longer the resistance continued, the tougher the men of the Waffen SS, the police and the army became; they fulfilled their tasks unstintingly as comrades in arms, doing their part in exemplary fashion. They were often in action from early in the morning until late at night."*
Final report by SS and Police Chief

● *"Our motto was: Live and die with dignity! In ghettos and camps, we tried to live up to this motto. Despite the greatest terror, the most extreme hunger and the bitterest poverty, we lived up to it until the martyrdom of Polish Jewry."*
Report by the Jewish Resistance Movement

14. Last Defenders Removed

15. The Ghetto is Destroyed

■ *"Only through the uninterrupted and untiring efforts of all forces did we succeed in capturing or exterminating 56,065 Jews. ... The operation ended on May 16, 1943 with the destruction of the Warsaw synagogue at 20:15.*
There are no more factories in the former Jewish district. All goods, raw materials and machines have been taken away and stored elsewhere. Everything in the way of buildings and the like has been destroyed."
Final report by the SS and Police Chief

Chronology

1942

January 21	First Jewish partisan organization created in Vilna
July 20	First armed resistance against ghetto evacuation in Nieswiez, Belorussia
July 20 to October 3	Mass deportations from the Warsaw Ghetto to extermination camps (310,000 people)
August 9	180 armed fighters escape from Mir ghetto, Belorussia, and join partisans in the forests
August 10	Attack on German garrison in Derechin, Belorussia, by Jewish partisan unit
August 16–18	Resistance against liquidation of Radom ghetto. 1500 people shot, the rest deported
September 2	Mass escape from Lachva ghetto, Belorussia. 120 fighters reach the forests
September 24–26	Armed resistance to liquidation of ghetto in Tutchin, Ukraine. Mass breakout
October	Jewish Fighting Organization (ZOB) founded in Warsaw

1943

January 18–23	First armed resistance against resumption of deportations in Warsaw
February 2	*German Sixth Army capitulates at Stalingrad*
February 5–12	10,000 people deported from Bialystok to Treblinka. 2,000 shot during the operation Attempts at self-defense in Czestochowa ghetto
April 19	Start of armed uprising against liquidation of Warsaw Ghetto
May 3	End of battle with SS and Wehrmacht
May 4–13	Bunkers defended until destruction
May 8	Military staff of the uprising falls in battle in the bunker at Mila Street 18
May 16	SS ends its "major operation". Last fighting continues until mid-July
June 1	Resistance to liquidation of ghetto in Lemberg. 3,000 people shot, the rest deported
June 25	Czestochowa ghetto liquidated; sporadic fighting
July 5–12	*Battle near Kursk: German offensive repulsed*
July 10	*Allied landing in Sicily*
July	Jewish partisan groups in the Wyszkower forests
August 1	Bedzin and Sosnowiec ghettos liquidated, tempts at Jewish self-defense
August 2	Revolt by Jewish special detail in Treblinka Prisoners escape; camp liquidated
August 15–22	Uprising and liquidation of Bialystok ghetto
September 1	Attempted uprising in Vilna ghetto. Fighters flee to the partisans
September 2	Jewish self-defense in Tarnow ghetto
October 14	Uprising in Sobibor, Prisoners escape; camp liquidated
October–December	Operations by Jewish partisan groups in the districts of Lublin, Bialystok, Cracow and Radom
November 3–5	Mass shootings of Jewish factory workers deported from Warsaw in Poniatowa, Trawniki and Maidanek (43,000 victims)
November 19	Revolt and attempted escape by Jewish prisoners of *Sonderkommando* 1005 in Janowska camp, Lemberg

13. The End of the War

By the time the Germans were defeated at Stalingrad, it had become evident to everyone that Hitler was losing the war. The Soviet Russian counteroffensive could no longer be halted.

After the conclusion of "Operation Reinhard," the physical annihilation of the Jews in the Generalgouvernement, the murderers tried to cover up all traces of their crimes. During 1943, the extermination camps at Belzec, Treblinka, and Sobibor were razed, the killing installations destroyed, and the camp grounds plowed up; farm houses were built and shrubs planted.

On Himmler's orders, "Special Commando 1005" was formed to eliminate vast mass graves adjacent to the extermination camp in Poland, and execution sites in the Soviet Union. Columns of Jewish prisoners, guarded by SS, had to dig up the partly decomposed corpses, place them on huge pyres, burn them, sift the soil, grind the remaining bones, and scatter the ashes. Then they were shot as witnesses, like their fellow sufferers in the death camps who had worked in the gas chambers or crematoria. There were to be no witnesses, dead or alive.

But this SS scheme proved unworkable. The mass graves were too numerous, the German retreat too rapid. Thus during its westward advance, the Red Army everywhere encountered huge pits full of corpses.

Despite the dramatically worsening war situation, the program of genocide continued with redoubled effort, as if the Nazis wished for a victory at least in this area. A race against time began. In June 1944, the Allied invasion began in Normandy. Simultaneously, nearly half a million people were deported from Hungary to Auschwitz.

On July 24, four days after the last unsuccessful attempt to assassinate Hitler and overthrow his regime, Red Army troops reached the Maidanek camp. By the end of August, the Americans were in Paris. But at Auschwitz, the gas chambers continued to operate until the end of October. Another three months would pass before the camp was liberated by Soviet soldiers.

1. The Tide Turns

Stalingrad

The battle at the Volga in winter 1942–43 ended in total military defeat for Hitler's army. It was the turning point of the war on the eastern front. The remnants of the German Sixth Army, 90,000 men, were taken prisoner by the Soviets.

The battle at the Kursk bend half a year later, the biggest tank battle in history, had even greater strategic significance. The last German attempt to advance failed, the Soviet counter offensive began.

2. Jewish Partisans

Wisnizka region, Ukraine, January 1943

Parallel to the Soviet offensive, partisan operations increased in the German-occupied areas of the Soviet Union and Poland; tens of thousands of Jews took part.

On September 8, 1943, the prisoners in the Italian internment camp on Rab Island liberated themselves. All Jewish prisoners who were still able to march joined the Yugoslav partisan army.

3. Discovery of Mass Graves

In 1943, the Reich Security Main Office created *Sonderkommando* [Special Commando] 1005. Jewish prisoners were forced to reopen the mass graves in Poland and the occupied areas of the Soviet Union and burn the corpses. Afterwards they were shot. The head of this "disinterring operation" was SS Corporal Blobel.

The rapid Soviet advance made it impossible, however, for the SS to erase all traces of the mass murders in time. Thus even as the war continued, Soviet investigative commissions began exhuming victims at the shooting pits. Blobel was condemned to death in 1948 and executed in Landsberg in 1951.

■ *"I, Paul Blobel, swear, declare and testify:*

1. I was born in Potsdam on August 13, 1894. From June 1941 to January 1942 I was head of Sonderkommando 4.

2. After I was relieved of this duty, I was told to report to SS Lieutenant General Heydrich and Group Leader Müller in Berlin, and was assigned the duty by Major General Müller in June 1942 of eliminating the traces of executions by the Einsatzgruppen in the East. My orders were to report personally to the commanders of the security police and SD and to pass Müller's order on to them orally and to supervise its execution. The order was top secret, and Major General Müller ordered that, because of the strict secrecy of this task, no correspondence could be held.

5. According to the order, my duties were to have covered the entire territory of the Einsatzgruppen; however, because of the retreat from Russia, I could not carry out my orders completely.

I have read the above statement, consisting of three pages, in German and declare that it is the whole truth to the best of my knowledge and belief. I had the opportunity to make changes and corrections in the above statement. I made this statement voluntarily, without any promise of reward, and I was subject to no force or threat."

Sworn statement by SS Colonel Paul Blobel in Nuremberg on June 18, 1947

4. Maidanek Liberated

Marshall N. A. Bulganin views the camp

On July 24, 1944, four days after the final, vain attempt to eliminate Hitler and overthrow his regime, Soviet troops liberated Maidanek concentration and extermination camp, near Lublin. A half million people from throughout Europe had passed through the camp.

Over 250,000 prisoners, mainly Poles, Jews and Russians, died here. They were gassed or shot, or died of exhaustion. The SS had no time to blow up the gas chambers and crematorium; thus the extermination camp was completely preserved.

5. Auschwitz, Summer 1944

The German Wehrmacht was in retreat on all fronts. On June 6, the Allies landed in Normandy, and on August 23 Paris was liberated. But the deportations to Auschwitz continued. The death camp at Chelmno even resumed operation.

When 437,000 deportees from Hungary arrived at Auschwitz within two months, those condemned to death often had to wait an entire day in the woods near crematorium V, outside the overfilled gas chambers.

flight give an idea of how cremation of the bodies from the mass graves must have proceeded.

6. Paris Liberated

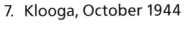
Paris, rue La Fayette, August 1944

7. Klooga, October 1944

As the front drew closer, the work camp Klooga in Estonia was evacuated. On September 19, 1944, nine days before liberation, 2,400 Jewish inmates and Soviet prisoners of war were shot.

The piles of bodies that the SS were unable to eliminate before their

8. Blowing up the Gas Chambers

In October 1944, some 700 prisoners still worked day and night shifts in the special details in the crematoria of Auschwitz-Birkenau. Not until the beginning of November did gassing end. At the end of the month, Himmler ordered the crematoria destroyed.

At the last roll call before evacuation on January 18, 1945, Auschwitz and

all its auxiliary camps contained 66,000 prisoners. On January 27, 7,000 who had been left behind because they were too weak to march were liberated by Red Army soldiers. The night before, the SS had blown up the last crematorium.

precipitous withdrawal left them no time to shoot the sick and those too weak to march.

The Red Army found 600 dead and 7,650 survivors when it liberated the camp, among them 100 children who had been left alive for use in medical experiments.

9. Auschwitz Liberated

Auschwitz, January 27, 1945

As the front approached, the SS "evacuated" the Auschwitz camp and drove 58,000 prisoners on death marches to the West. Many died. The

10.

Chronology

1944

March 15	*Soviet troops cross the Bug*
March 19	*German troops invade Hungary*
March 29	Racial laws introduced in Hungary
April 10	*Transnistria, Bukowina and Bessarabia liberated*
April 14	First transports of Jews from Athens to Auschwitz
April 15	Escape attempt by Jewish prisoners in Ponary camp near Vilna
May 15–July 9	437,000 Jews deported from Hungary to Auschwitz
June 4	*The Allies arrive in Rome*
June 6	*Allied landing in Normandy*
June 23	*Beginning of second Soviet offensive*
	Chelmno death camp again operational
July 20	*Last unsuccessful attempt on Hitler's life*
July 24	Soviet troops liberate Maidanek concentration camp
July 25	Kovno ghetto liquidated
July 29	*Soviet troops on the Vistula*
August 1– October 2	Uprising by "Polish Home Army" in Warsaw
August 2– September 15	Lodz ghetto dissolved. 68,500 people deported to Auschwitz
August 6	27,000 Jews deported from camps east of the Vistula to Germany; Kaiserswald camp (Riga) "evacuated"
August 23	*Paris liberated. Romania capitulates*
August 28–29	National revolt in Slovakia. Liberated Jewish prisoners join partisans
September	New deportations from Theresienstadt to Auschwitz
	Final transport from France to Auschwitz
September 11	*British troops reach Holland*
September 13	*Soviet troops on the Slovakian border*
September 14	*American troops on the German border*
September 23	Mass executions in Klooga camp, Estonia.
	Renewed deportations from Slovakia
September 30– October 30	Eleven transports from Theresienstadt to Birkenau (18,404 prisoners)
October 6–7	Auschwitz-Birkenau: uprising of prisoners in the *Sonderkommando* [special commando]. One crematorium destroyed
October 18	*Hitler orders creation of the "Volkssturm"*
end of October	Last gassings in Auschwitz-Birkenau
November	Trial of the staff of the Maidanek extermination camp in Lublin
November 3	*Soviet troops approach Budapest*
November 8–18	38,000 Jews deported from Budapest to concentration camps in Germany
November 26	Himmler orders destruction of gas chambers and crematoria

14. Liberation of the Camps

During the first four months of 1945, events followed in rapid succession. As the Allied armies advanced on Germany from all sides, the German population of entire provinces fled before the approaching eastern front. But at the same time the surviving prisoners in the camps, desperately awaiting the hour of liberation, were dragged off by the SS into the interior of the country.

Concentration camps close to the approaching front lines were abandoned one by one, their inmates evacuated, those unable to march killed on the spot. The SS drove columns of prisoners along the roads in forced marches; anyone who collapsed was shot by the guards. Others were transported in freight trains from one camp to the next. When these erratic journeys finally ended days later, many had died of cold or hunger. In the Bergen-Belsen camp, the final destination of most of the prisoner transports, all attempts at provisioning collapsed. Tens of thousands perished here, shortly before liberation and in the first few days that followed.

A glimpse of Hell awaited the Allied soldiers who liberated the remaining concentration camps in the spring of 1945. Everywhere -- at Buchenwald, Mauthausen, and Dachau -- they were confronted with identical scenes: thousands of dead and dying. English and American army doctors discovered too late the awful fact that many who might have been saved had died because they were too weak to call out or even raise an arm; they thus went unnoticed among the corpses.

The Allied victory kept the National Socialist regime from carrying its program of genocide to its ultimate conclusion. Yet the outcome was horrifying enough. All historical investigations and calculations agree that between five and six million Jews were killed. More than a million met their deaths in ghettos and camps; at least as many died in mass executions, the remainder perished in the gas chambers.

1. Searching for the Missing

(see next page)

2. Death Marches

In January 1945, the SS began to evacuate the concentration camps in the east to prevent their liberation by the Red Army. Where no train transport could be arranged, the prisoners were driven westwards in forced marches.

The columns passed through numerous German towns. Thousands died on the march from exhaustion or were shot.

Dachau prisoners on the march, Grünwald, April 29, 1945

3. Death Transports

Arrival at Dachau 1945

■ *"One day, without prior notification, Lieutenant General Pohl sent me 6,000 women and children who had been in the transport for ten days without food. They were transported in December 1944 in an icy winter in open coal cars without blankets. According to orders from Berlin, I had to march the children to Bergen-Belsen, and I assume they all died....*

I give as an example a transport that left with 4,500 people and arrived at Mauthausen with 180. Women and children were without shoes, in rags and full of lice. In the transport were whole families, of whom countless were shot on the way because of general weakness."

Testimony of the commandant of Mauthausen, Franz Ziereis, 1945

In der Nacht vom 20-21.1.44 aus der Wohnung CC-380
Promenade des Anglais, NYONS - Drôme von der Gestapo
verhaftet und zum Fort Montluc - LYON transportiert
vom 28.1.44 bis 3.2.44 Aufenthalt in Drancy bei PARIS
ab 3.2.44 deportiert, ohne jede Nachricht.
vH. Nachrichten an Louis LAZAR, NYONS (Drôme) France

LAZAR Berthe
née Salmon
né le 5.2.1903

LAZAR Ruth
né le 20.4.1926

LAZAR Günther
né le 12.9.1927

LAZAR Kurt
né le 21.3.1931

LAZAR Francine
né le 23.6.1939

STRAUSS Werner
né le 24.10.1928

"Arrested by the Gestapo on the night of January 20–21, 1944 from apartment on Promenade des Anglais, Nyons-Drome, and deported to Port Montluc-Lyon; in Drancy near Paris from January 28 to February 3, deported on February 3, 1944 with no news. Any information to Louis Lazar, Nyons (Drome), France.

Lazar, Berthe, nee Salmon, born February 5, 1903	Lazar, Kurt, born March 21, 1931
Lazar, Ruth, born April 20, 1926	Lazar, Francine, June 23, 1939
Lazar, Günther, born September 12, 1927	Strauss, Werner, born October 24, 1928."

Louis Lazar's inquest of his family

4. The Yalta Conference

Churchill, Roosevelt and Stalin, February 1945

At the Yalta Conference, the Allies decided on:
1. Better coordination of military planning,
2. Division of Germany into four zones of occupation and creation of an Allied Control Council,
3. Demilitarization and denazification, dissolution of the Wehrmacht and the NSDAP, destruction of the armaments industry, prosecution of all German war criminals,
4. Imposition of reparations,
5. Shifting of Poland's borders to the west,
6. Recognition of the "Lublin Committee" as the provisional Polish government,
7. Conference on founding the United Nations,
8. Entry of the USSR into the war against Japan.

5. Survivors

● *"It was impossible to get their names out of them. The kindest words had no power to bring them to speech. A long, fixed, expressionless gaze was all. When they tried to answer, their tongues couldn't reach their palates to produce a sound.*

One was only aware of their poisonous breath; it seemed to come from their entrails, which were already in a state of decomposition. That is how the transports looked in the winter of 1944–45, in a winter that claimed the monstrous total of 13,000 of the interned in the last three months before our liberation."

Report by Dr. Georg Straka,
prisoner in Bergen-Belsen

Wöbbelin

6. Buchenwald

▲ *"All were in a state of complete emaciation. The American authorities informed us that the death toll had sunk since their arrival from some 100 to 35 per day. Usual clothing was a torn coat, vest or cotton jacket, under which one could see thighs no thicker than normal wrists....*

The medical members of our delegation were convinced that a certain percentage would not survive, even with the treatment they now enjoyed, and that an even larger percentage that could survive would probably be ill and unable to work for the rest of their lives."

Report from Buchenwald by a British parliamentary delegation, April 1945

7. Mauthausen

Ebensee subsidiary camp, May 7, 1945

8. Bergen-Belsen

● *"It was hard to tell who was dead and who was still alive. We all looked so alike.*
Right down to the bones of emaciated bodies, and in the eyes that enigmatic, horrified expression. No one buried the dead."

Zdenka Vantlova, former prisoner in Bergen-Belsen

● *"The guards in the concentration camps -- I am speaking of all the camps -- are like wild animals, and in the course of time the prisoners also became animals. In such a place, human goodness is entirely unknown."*

H. O. Le Druillenec, former prisoner in Bergen-Belsen

137

9. Involuntary Visitors

Following the liberation of Buchenwald, on the orders of the American occupying force, 1,000 residents of Weimar between the ages of 18 and 45 years old, half men and half women, including many members of the Nazi Party, were brought to the Ettersberg and led through the concentration camp.

Wöbellin Camp

Buchenwald, April 16, 1945

▲ *". . . Women fainted. Men covered their faces and turned their heads away. When the civilians cried out again and again, 'We didn't know! We didn't know!', the liberated prisoners were beside themselves with fury. 'You knew!', they screamed."*

Margaret Bourke-White, reporter for Life Magazine

10. The Liberated

American doctors determined that the prisoners weighed an average of between 28 and 36 kilograms.

Most had lost 50–60 percent of their body weight and had shrunk to below normal size. Many survivors did not have the strength to stand, and lay apathetically in their barracks. Those who could still walk had to help bury their dead comrades and care for those who survived.

11. Captured SS Guards

SS-guards, Belsen

12. A First Meal

The British army cleared the camp. Because of acute danger of epidemic, the dead were thrown into hurriedly-dug graves, the typhus barracks burned down, the sick taken to hospitals. The few healthy survivors attempted to return to a normal routine. They washed for the first time in many weeks.

Women curled their hair, if they still had any. Others sought suitable clothing. Some cooked their first soup on a small fire of wood clogs. The camp commandant and the all-powerful guards, until recently masters of life and death, were taken into British custody.

13. Returning to Life

Bergen-Belsen

14. The Buchenwald Oath

Hovel at Buchenwald

● *"We will only end the struggle when the last guilty one stands before the judges of nations. The destruction of Nazism at the roots is our slogan! The creation of a new world in peace and freedom is our goal! We owe this to our murdered comrades and their families."*

Oath by the prisoners of Buchenwald, April 1945

▲ *"German militarism and Nazism will be stamped out, and in joint agreement in the present and future, the Allies will also take further measures necessary so that Germany can never again threaten its neighbors or the preservation of peace throughout the world."*

Official announcement on the Potsdam conference by the victorious powers, August 2, 1945

15. Mass Graves at Bergen-Belsen

● *"Turn your eyes to the hills of bodies, observer of history; pause for only a moment and imagine that these poor remains of flesh and bone are your father, your child, your wife, the person you love! You yourself and those closest to you, to whom you are attached with heart and soul, see them thrown naked in the filth, tormented, starving, dead."*

Eugen Kogon, author and former political prisoner

▲ *"We also honor the German heroes of Dachau and Buchenwald: those Christians, Jews, communists, socialists, liberals, pacifists, and the simple men and women against whom Hitler aimed his hatred, without defeating them. For God sees them, I firmly believe, as history will see them, side by side with the dead of our own people . . ."*

Victor Gollancz

16.

▲ *"With street plows, General Dempsey's soldiers dug long graves, in each of which 500 or 1,000 bodies could be buried. Then the former guards -- men and women -- had to carry over the corpses of those who had died of epidemic, starvation, suffocation or shooting.*
It took a week before it got to the point that the piles of bodies stopped growing, because they could finally be buried in the mass graves as quickly as they were dying."

Report by American Information Service, 1945

17. Berlin, May 1945

Reichstag building, Berlin

● *"There are two types of guilt: systematically committing a crime, and making it possible and permitting it. We didn't want this and didn't know that. But it was up to us to have wanted and to have known. . . .*
Will the Germans, after such a horrible lesson, draw the good, neces-

sary and salutary conclusions that will make us real Germans -- that is, Europeans?"
Alfred Döblin, 1946

18. The Nuremberg Trial

1st row: 1. Hermann Göring, 2. Rudolf Hess, 3. Joachim von Ribbentrop, 4. Wilhelm Keitel, 5. Ernst Kaltenbrunner, 6. Alfred Rosenberg, 7. Hans Frank, 8. Wilhelm Frick, 9. Julius Streicher, 10. Walther Funk, 11. Hjalmar Schacht
2nd row: 1. Karl Dönitz, 2. Erich Raeder, 3. Baldur von Schirach, 4. Fritz Sauckel, 5. Alfred Jodl, 6. Franz von Papen, 7. Arthur Seyss-Inquart, 8. Albert Speer, 9. Constantin von Neurath, 10. Hans Fritzsche

▲ *"The last forty years of the twentieth century will be reckoned in history books to the bloodiest of all time. No half century ever saw such slaughter, such cruelty and inhumanity, such mass deportations of peoples into slavery, such extermination of minorities. The horrors of Torquemada pale before the Nazi inquisition.*
These deeds are somber historical facts that will recall this century to future generations. If we are not able to eliminate the causes of these *barbaric events and prevent their repetition, then it is most likely not an irresponsible prophecy to say that this twentieth century may still succeed in bringing the downfall of civilization."*
Robert H. Jackson, chief American prosecutor at Nuremberg

19. Epilogue

Jewish cemetery, Federal Republic of Germany

Schoolgirls from Israel and Germany, Auschwitz

Chronology

1945

January 18	Last roll call at Auschwitz and its subsidiary camps: 66,020 prisoners. Beginning of death march to the west
January 19	Lodz liberated. 870 Jews survived in hiding
January 25	Evacuation of Stutthof and subsidiaries. Of 50,000 prisoners, more than half die on the death march
January 27	Red Army liberates Auschwitz. It finds 7,650 prisoners left behind
February 4–11	*Conference at Yalta in the Crimea*
February 16	Decree on destruction of all "dejudaization files," when they can no longer be removed
March 5	*American troops on the Rhine*
March 19	*Hitler orders destruction of all supply, industrial and transport facilities in Germany*
April 10	"Evacuation" (death march) of 15,000 Jews from Buchenwald
April 11	Buchenwald prisoners liberate themselves. American troops take over camp
April 15	Bergen-Belsen liberated by British troops
April 20	"Evacuation" of prisoners from Sachsenhausen begins
April 22	Sachsenhausen liberated by Red Army
April 23	Beginning of "evacuation" of prisoners from Ravensbrück. Last massacre by SS guards
April 25	*American and Soviet troops meet on the Elbe*
April 29	Dachau liberated by American troops
April 30	Ravensbrück liberated by the Red Army. *Hitler commits suicide*
May 2	*Berlin capitulates*
May 3	Theresienstadt taken over by International Red Cross
May 5	Mauthausen liberated
May 8	*Unconditional surrender of Germany: end of the war in Europe*
May 23	*Himmler commits suicide while being arrested*
June 26	*Founding of the United Nations*
July 17–	
August 2	*Potsdam Conference*
August 6	*First atomic bomb dropped on Hiroshima*
August 9	*Atom bomb dropped on Nagasaki*
August 15	*Japan capitulates: end of the Second World War*
November 14	*Beginning of Nuremberg Trial*

History of the Building

1. Villa Marlier

The building seen from the street, 1916

The villa was built in 1914–15 by the merchant, factory owner, and Privy Commercial Councilor Ernst Marlier. Paul O. A. Baumgarten, a student of Alfred Messels, designed both the building, which contained 1,500 square meters of living space, and the large garden, which measured 30,000 square meters and was nearly a park. Baumgarten had already built several villas nearby, among them one for the painter Max Liebermann in 1909. Ernst Marlier and his wife Margarete lived at Wannsee for only a few years. He sold the house and premises on September 6, 1921, to a firm belonging to the industrialist Friedrich Minoux.

2. Friedrich Minoux

Friedrich Minoux (1877–1945) began his career in 1900 with the Essen Gas and Water Works. In 1912, he entered the service of the industrial magnate Hugo Stinnes and became a managing director of his business in 1919. On February 21, 1923, he mediated an unsuccessful discussion in the villa between the chief of the Army command, General Hans von Seeckt, and the former quartermaster general, Erich Ludendorff, on possible measures to be taken against the occupation of the Ruhr region. In fall 1923, Minoux was considered as a possible member of a dictatorial "Directory" that was to replace the elected Reich government. On October 25, 1923, he met with Ludendorff and Hitler in Munich, but they reached no agreement on a common plan for the attempted Putsch of November 9, 1923.

Dining room with winter garden, around 1922

3. The Nordhav Foundation

After Stinnes and Minoux had parted ways in fall 1923, Minoux opened a wholesale coal firm. Between 1924 and 1938, he exploited his position as a member of the board of GASAG [utility company] to defraud the company, together with two accomplices, of at least twelve million Reichsmark. Suspicions were first aroused in 1935, but Minoux succeeded in delaying criminal proceedings against him until 1937, and was not arrested until May 1940. He started to serve his five year sentence in Brandenburg penitentiary in June 1942. In summer 1945 he returned to Berlin, where he died shortly thereafter.

Minoux had sold the villa in November 1940 to the Nordhav SS Foundation set up by Heydrich. The purpose of the foundation was to build and maintain vacation resorts for the SS Security Service (SD). However, the first purchase the foundation made, in 1939, was a large landed estate on the island of Fehmarn, close to where Heydrich had his vacation home. He obviously wanted to retain both the estate and the Wannsee villa on a long-term basis for private and official purposes. In his capacity as Head of the Reich Security Main Office, or conceivably in an even higher political position, he wanted ultimately to use them for official functions and as a holiday resort.

4. Sale of the Premises

Friedrich Minoux was not forced to sell. The Nordhav Foundation paid him 1.95 million Reichsmark, the market price. The SS also took over part of the furnishings, among them the dining room with a Gobelin. Converted into a guest house in summer 1941, the building was at the disposal of primarily out-of-town police and SS officers from October 1941 on. On January 20,1942, Reinhard Heydrich chaired here the meeting that subsequently became known as the "Wannsee Conference".

5. SS Guest House

After Heydrich's death in June 1942, the foundation saw no further need to maintain such a spacious and costly building. On February 4, 1943, it sold the house to the Reich Security Main Office for the same price it had paid to Minoux. The stated purpose was the preservation of the building as a recreation center for men and officers of the Security Police.

At the end of 1944, SS officers and officials of the Reich Ministry of the Interior discussed here the "plans of the participants in the plot of July 20, pertaining to reforms of state and administration!" Their deliberations were based on a memorandum written by the resistance fighter Fritz-Dieflof Count von der Schulenburg, who had been executed on August 10, 1944.

"What does the guest house offer?

Completely renovated guestrooms, communal rooms such as music rooms, gamerooms (billiards), a large hall and winter garden, terraces facing the Wannsee, central heating, running water and all the amenities.

The house contains a good kitchen that provides lunch and dinner; wine, beer and tobacco products are available.

The fact that the guest house is outside the city center presents no problems for the visitor, as a car is available for trips to and from the Wannsee train station. Call for pickup at any time, at 80 57 60.

Wannsee train station can be reached from all Berlin train stations by S-Bahn in a short time (Friedrichstrasse Station, around 20 minutes; Potsdam and Anhalter Stations, around 25 minutes).

Prices, including maid service and breakfast, is 5 RM per night. We ask that you make as much use of the guest house facilities as possible, so that the house becomes a center of comradely traffic for the outside SS leaders of the security police and the SD in Berlin."

Order Bulletin of the Chief of the Security Police and SD, 2nd volume, no. 45, Berlin, November 15, 1941.

6. The Postwar Period

In 1945, the house was inhabited first by Soviet Russian marines, thereafter by American officers. In 1947, the August Bebel Institute of the Social Democratic Party turned it into a residential adult education center, and from 1952 until 1988, the building served as a school hostel for the district of Neukölln.
It is largely owing to the historian Joseph Wulf that the villa became publicly known as the location of the Wannsee Conference. In 1965, Wulf suggested to establish here an 'International Documents Center for the Study of National Socialism and its Consequences'.

Class of pupils from Berlin/Neukölln, April 1952

7. Joseph Wulf's Legacy

Nahum Goldmann and Joseph Wulf
in the Villa, October 1966

Wulf's plans gained prominent advocates. Nahum Goldmann, President of the World Jewish Congress, offered substantial financial support if such a document center were established at this historic site. But the Berlin government was not willing to make the building available to Wulf. After years of unsuccessful negotiations, the Association for a Document Center dissolved in 1972. Joseph Wulf committed suicide in fall 1974. Not until two decades later, in January 1992, on the 50th anniversary of the Wannsee Conference, was the house formally inaugurated as a memorial and educational site.

Sources

Archives, agencies: A.D.N. Bildarchiv • Amtsgericht Berlin-Schöneberg • Archiv des Diakonischen Werkes, Berlin • Archiv zur Geschichte der Max-Planck-Gesellschaft • Argon Verlag, Berlin • Association du Musée de la Résistance Nationale, Ivry-sur-Seine • Associazione Nazionale ex Deportati Politici nei Campi Nazisti (A.N.E.D.), Mailand • Bayerisches Hauptstaatsarchiv, München • Belgium Radio & TV, Brüssel • Berlin Document Center • Beth Hatefutsoth, Tel Aviv • Bibliothèque Historique, Paris • Bibliothèque Nationale, Paris • Bildarchiv Abraham Pisarek, Berlin • Bildarchiv Preussischer Kulturbesitz, Berlin • Bildstelle Hanau • BRTN, Omroep van de Vlaamse Gemeenschap, Brüssel • Bundesarchiv Koblenz/Potsdam • Centre de Documentation Juive Contemporaine, Paris • Deutsche Presse-Agentur GmbH, Frankfurt/Main • Deutsches Historisches Museum, Berlin • La Documentation Française, Paris • Dokumentationsarchiv des Österreichischen Widerstandes, Wien • Éditions Tallandier/Photothèque, Paris • Fondation Auschwitz, Brüssel • Památnik Terezín, Theresienstadt • G.A.U. (Staatliche Archiv-Verwaltung), Moskau • Gedenkstätte Deutscher Widerstand, Berlin • Glówna Komisja Badania Zbrodni Hitlerowskich w Polsce/Instytut Pamieci Narodowej, Warschau • Historisches Museum der Stadt Wien • Hulton Deutsch, London • Imperial War Museum, London • IML/ZPA (SAPMO), Berlin • Institute of Contemporary History and Wiener Library, London • Jüdisches Museum, Belgrad • Jüdisches Museum, Berlin • Jüdisches Museum, Frankfurt/Main • Beate Klarsfeld Fondation, Paris • Landesarchiv Berlin • Landesbildstelle Berlin • Leo Baeck Institute, New York • Ministère des Affaires Etrangères, Paris • National Archives, Washington • Niedersächsisches Staatsarchiv, Aurich • Novosti Presseagentur, Moskau • Österreichische Gesellschaft für Zeitgeschichte, Wien • Panstwowe Muzeum Oświęcim-Brzezinka, Auschwitz • Politisches Archiv des Auswärtigen Amtes, Bonn • Rijksinstituut voor Oorlogsdocumentatie, Amsterdam • Agence Roger-Viollet, Paris • Sovfoto Warschau • Staatsanwaltschaft Düsseldorf • Staatsarchiv Nürnberg • Stadtarchive Berlin, Bielefeld, Euskirchen, Eisenach, Siegburg, Stuttgart, Würzburg • Anne Frank Stichting, Amsterdam • Stiftung Topographie des Terrors, Berlin • Süddeutscher Verlag, München • Der Tagesspiegel, Berlin • Ullstein Bilderdienst, Berlin • U. S. Holocaust Memorial Museum, Washington D. C. • Yad Vashem, Jerusalem • Zentrale Stelle der Landesjustizverwaltungen, Ludwigsburg • Żydówski Instytut Históryczny w Polsce, Warschau.

Photographers: Georg W. Fossum s. A., Oslo • Mendel Grossmann s. A., Lodz • Eugen Heilig • Peter Heilmann, Berlin • Fredy Neff, Brühl bei Köln • Abraham Pisarek s. A., Berlin • Dirk Reinartz, Buxtehude • Henryk Ross s. A., Lodz • David Rubiner, Jerusalem • Herbert Sonnenfeld s. A., Berlin.

Private collections: Annegret Ehmann, Berlin • Carl Gustav Friedrichsen, Oldenburg • Günther Bernd Ginzel, Köln • Helge Grabitz, Hamburg • Wolfgang Scheffler, Berlin • Gerhard Schoenberner, Berlin • Isaac E. Wahler, Alten-Buseck.